It's Another Ace Book from CGP

This book is for 9-10 year olds.

It covers all the <u>really important bits</u> in the Literacy Strategy at the word and sentence levels.

It's been written for use in class or as a homework aid, to revise all the key stuff covered in the Literacy Hour.

And it's just as good for parents — the ideal way to give your child that extra bit of help with their English.

CGP are just the best

The central aim of Coordination Group Publications is to produce top quality books that are carefully written, immaculately presented and marvellously funny — whilst always making sure they exactly cover the National Curriculum for each subject.

And then we supply them to as many people as we possibly can, as <u>cheaply</u> as we possibly can.

Buy our books — they're ace

Contents

Published by Coordination Group Publications Ltd.

Contributors:
Simon Cook   BA (Hons)
Taissa Csáky   BA (Hons)
Gemma Hallam   BA (Hons)
Simon Little   BA (Hons)
Iain Nash   BSc
Andy Park BSc (Hons)
Glenn Rogers   BSc (Hons)

ISBN   1-84146-157-1

Groovy website: www.cgpbooks.co.uk

Jolly bits of clipart from CorelDRAW

Printed by Elanders Hindson, Newcastle upon Tyne.

Syllables

Syllables are the separate beats in a word. You could clap your hands once for each syllable in a word.

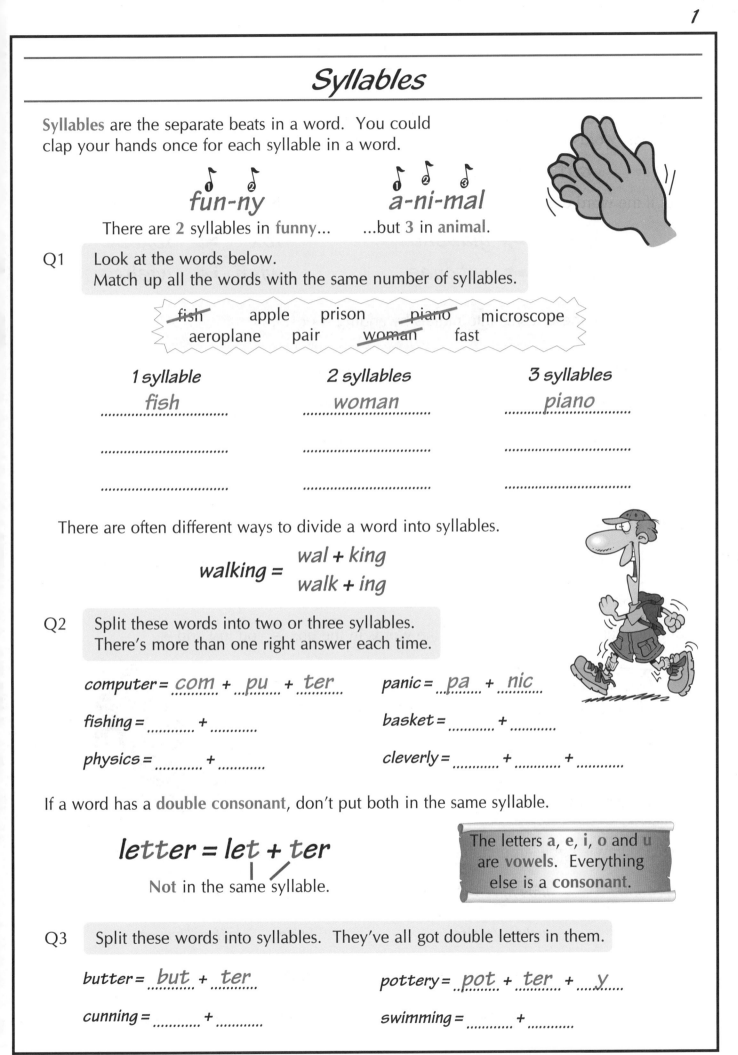

fun-ny

There are **2** syllables in **funny**...

a-ni-mal

...but **3** in **animal**.

Q1 Look at the words below.
Match up all the words with the same number of syllables.

~~fish~~ apple prison ~~piano~~ microscope
aeroplane pair ~~woman~~ fast

1 syllable	*2 syllables*	*3 syllables*
fish	*woman*	*piano*

There are often different ways to divide a word into syllables.

walking =
wal + king
walk + ing

Q2 Split these words into two or three syllables.
There's more than one right answer each time.

computer = *com* + *pu* + *ter* *panic =* *pa* + *nic*

fishing = _____ + _____ *basket =* _____ + _____

physics = _____ + _____ *cleverly =* _____ + _____ + _____

If a word has a **double consonant**, don't put both in the same syllable.

letter = let + ter

Not in the same syllable.

> The letters **a**, **e**, **i**, **o** and **u** are **vowels**. Everything else is a **consonant**.

Q3 Split these words into syllables. They've all got double letters in them.

butter = *but* + *ter* *pottery =* *pot* + *ter* + *y*

cunning = _____ + _____ *swimming =* _____ + _____

Plurals

You need to use a **plural** if there's more than one of something.
For most words you just add **-s** to the end of the word to make it plural.

$$cat \implies cats$$

But if the word ends in these **hissing sounds** — **-s**, **-sh**, **-ch** or **-x**, you have to add **-es**.

$$glass \implies glasses \qquad fox \implies foxes$$
$$witch \implies witches \qquad wish \implies wishes$$

Q1   Make these words into plurals by adding **-s** or **-es**.

dog	_dogs_	dress	_dresses_
ditch	....	bush	....
compass	....	branch	....
box	....	helmet	....

If the word ends in **-f** or **-fe**, you **nearly always** have to change these letters to **-ves**.

$$loaf \implies loaves \qquad wife \implies wives$$

Take off the -f...   ...and add -ves.   Take off the -fe...   ...and add -ves.

But there are some **odd ones**. For the words in the box — you just add -s.

roof → roofs
chief → chiefs
dwarf → dwarfs
belief → beliefs
proof → proofs

The chiefs met the dwarfs to discuss their beliefs.

Q2   Draw a circle around the correct plurals of these words.

life	lifes / (lives)		proof	(proofs) / prooves
wolf	wolves / wolfs		knife	knifes / knives
loaf	loafs / loaves		roof	rooves / roofs
wife	wives / wifes		chief	chiefs / chieves

Plurals

If a word ends in -y, you have to look at the letter **before** the -y.

toy → *toys*   *fairy* → *fairies*

vowel   consonant

If the letter before the -y is a **vowel** — just add -s.

If the letter before the -y is a **consonant** — take off the -y and add -**ies**.

The letters **a, e, i, o** and **u** are **vowels**. Everything else is a **consonant**.

Q3 Put a tick next to the plural if it's right but a cross next to it if it's wrong. If it's wrong, write what it should be.

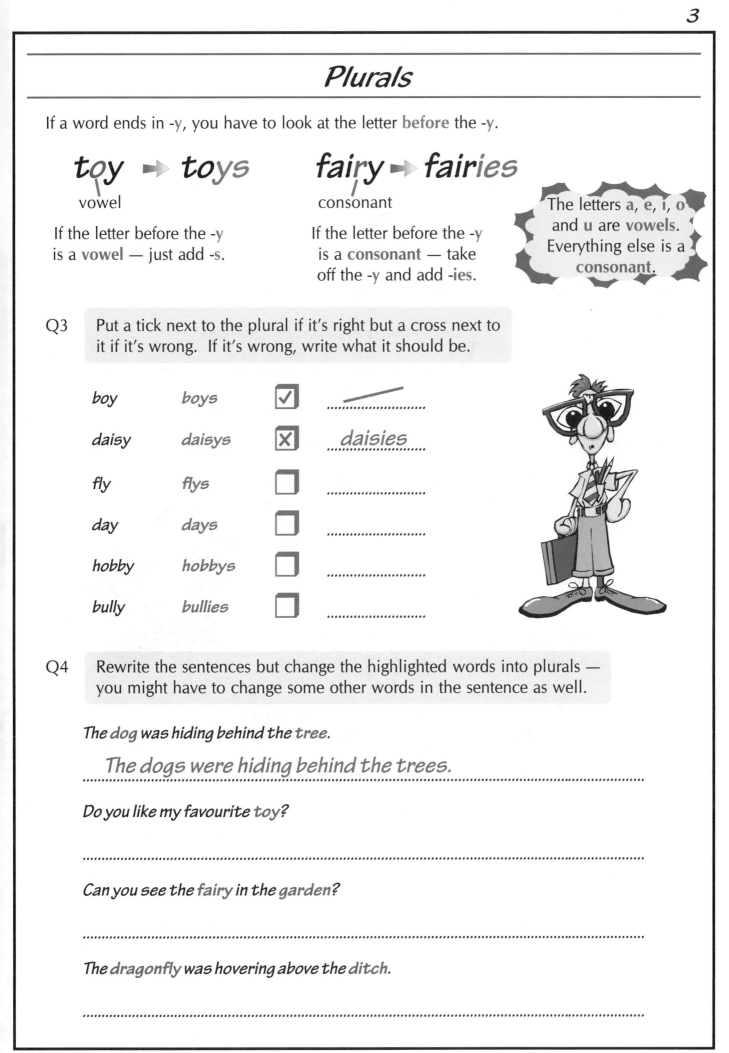

boy	*boys*	☑	_____
daisy	*daisys*	☒	*daisies*
fly	*flys*	☐	....
day	*days*	☐	....
hobby	*hobbys*	☐	....
bully	*bullies*	☐	....

Q4 Rewrite the sentences but change the highlighted words into plurals — you might have to change some other words in the sentence as well.

*The **dog** was hiding behind the **tree**.*

  The dogs were hiding behind the trees.

....

*Do you like my favourite **toy**?*

....

*Can you see the **fairy** in the **garden**?*

....

*The **dragonfly** was hovering above the **ditch**.*

....

Prefixes

Prefixes are groups of letters that go at the start of some words.
They change the meaning of the word.

tele*vision*   *trans*form

These are prefixes.

The prefix **tele-** means from a long way away.

Q1   Draw a line from these words to the right explanation.

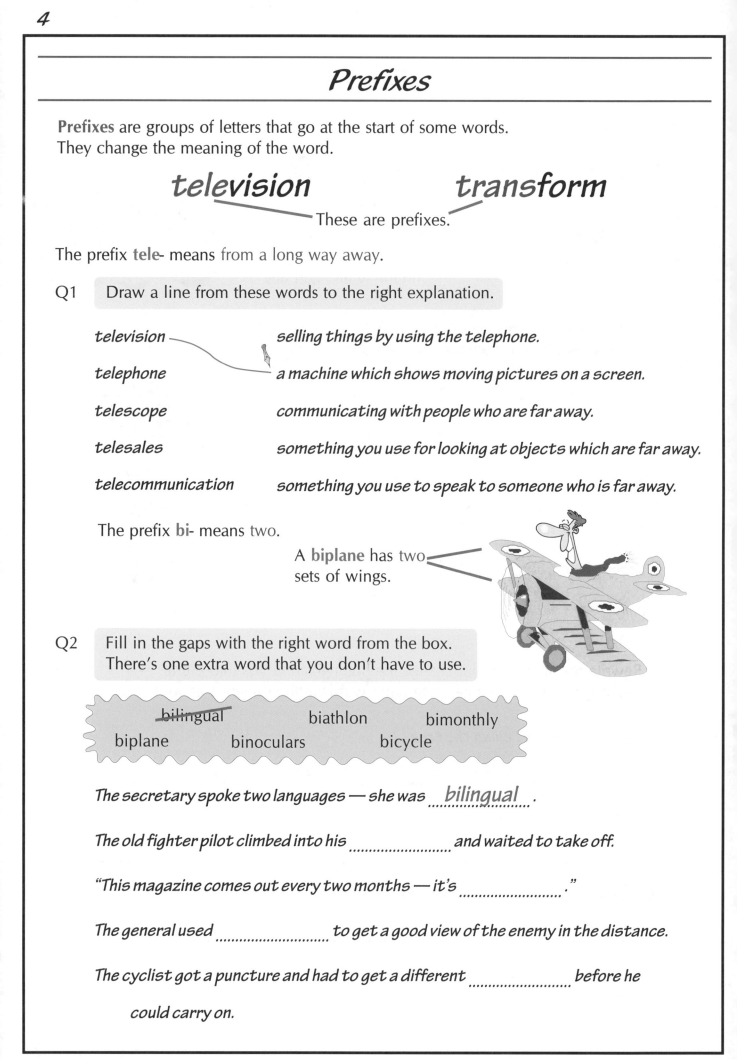

television   *selling things by using the telephone.*

telephone   *a machine which shows moving pictures on a screen.*

telescope   *communicating with people who are far away.*

telesales   *something you use for looking at objects which are far away.*

telecommunication   *something you use to speak to someone who is far away.*

The prefix **bi-** means two.

A **biplane** has two sets of wings.

Q2   Fill in the gaps with the right word from the box.
There's one extra word that you don't have to use.

~~bilingual~~	biathlon	bimonthly
biplane	binoculars	bicycle

The secretary spoke two languages — she was <u>bilingual</u> .

The old fighter pilot climbed into his .... *and waited to take off.*

"This magazine comes out every two months — it's .... *."*

The general used .... *to get a good view of the enemy in the distance.*

The cyclist got a puncture and had to get a different .... *before he*

    could carry on.

Prefixes

The prefix **trans-** means across or on the other side of.

trans-

The prefix **circum-** means around.

circum-

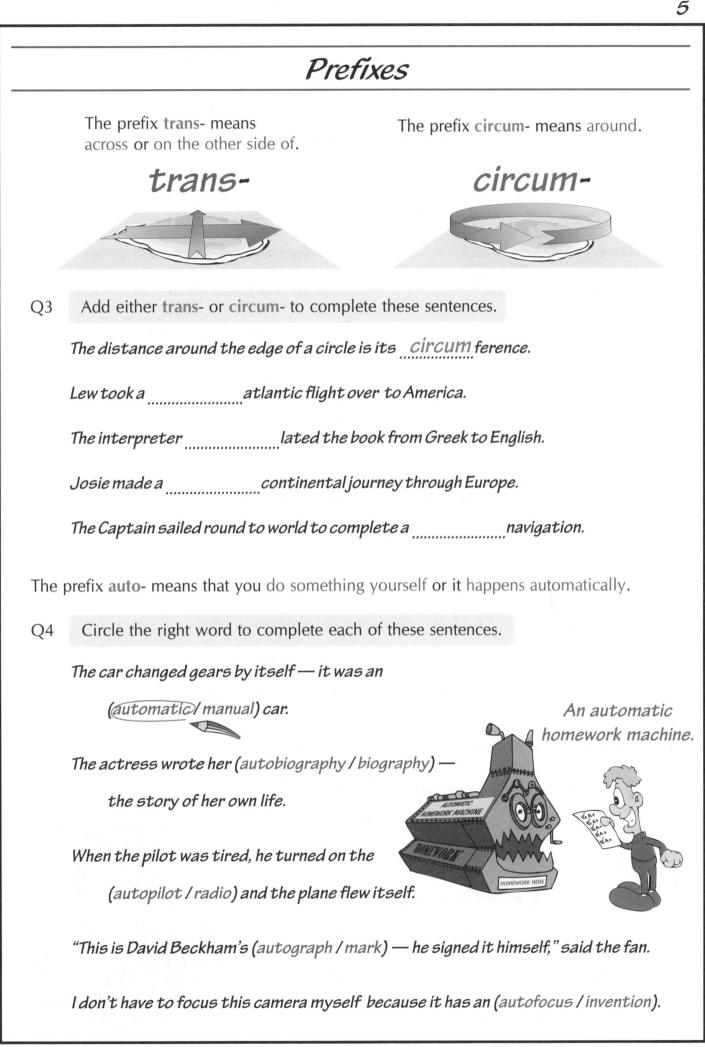

Q3 Add either **trans-** or **circum-** to complete these sentences.

The distance around the edge of a circle is its _circum_ ference.

Lew took a .... atlantic flight over to America.

The interpreter .... lated the book from Greek to English.

Josie made a .... continental journey through Europe.

The Captain sailed round to world to complete a .... navigation.

The prefix **auto-** means that you do something yourself or it happens automatically.

Q4 Circle the right word to complete each of these sentences.

The car changed gears by itself — it was an

(automatic / manual) car.

The actress wrote her (autobiography / biography) —

the story of her own life.

An automatic homework machine.

When the pilot was tired, he turned on the

(autopilot / radio) and the plane flew itself.

"This is David Beckham's (autograph / mark) — he signed it himself," said the fan.

I don't have to focus this camera myself because it has an (autofocus / invention).

Verbs

A **verb** is an **action word** in a sentence.

I play football every day.

'**Play**' is the action word or verb.

Q1   Draw a circle around the verbs in these sentences.

Doris (studies) every day.   Jess does her homework after dinner.

The film lasts an hour.   Boris goes to ballet lessons at the weekend.

Edna reads every day.   Dan cooks dinner in the kitchen.

You have to use the right form of a verb.
Use one form with **I, we, you** and **they**. Use a different form with **he, she** and **it**.

Examples:

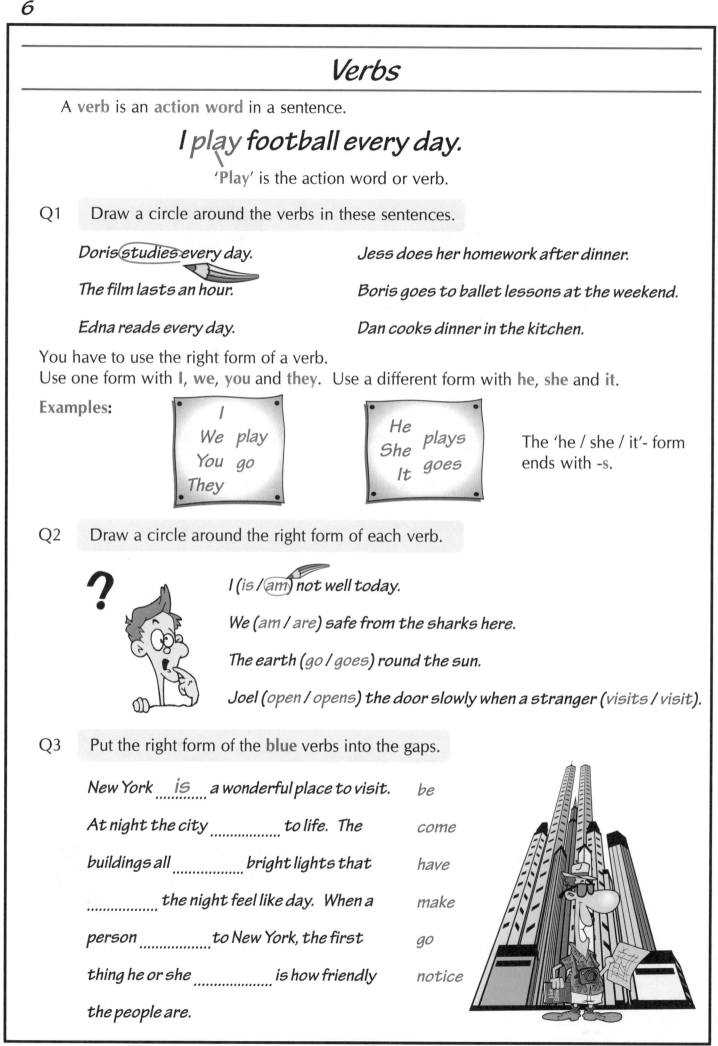

I
We play
You go
They

He
She plays
It goes

The 'he / she / it'- form ends with **-s**.

Q2   Draw a circle around the right form of each verb.

I (is / (am)) not well today.

We (am / are) safe from the sharks here.

The earth (go / goes) round the sun.

Joel (open / opens) the door slowly when a stranger (visits / visit).

Q3   Put the right form of the **blue** verbs into the gaps.

New York __is__ a wonderful place to visit.   be

At night the city _____ to life. The   come

buildings all _____ bright lights that   have

_____ the night feel like day. When a   make

person _____ to New York, the first   go

thing he or she _____ is how friendly   notice

the people are.

Simplifying Sentences

You can make a sentence easier for someone to understand if you use an **easy word** instead of a more difficult one.

That hat looks ridiculous.

That hat looks silly.

Q1 Draw a circle around the word that is easier for people to understand.

(say)   declare   make   assemble

attempt   try   watch   spectate

consider   think   happen   occur

You can sometimes make a complicated sentence easier to understand by **leaving out** words which aren't as important.

The man was old, and he was ugly like a horrible warty troll.

➡ *The man was old and ugly.*

Q2 Put one word in each gap to make a new clear sentence that means almost the same as each long one.

Jed could not get the piano to move; it was just too heavy and he could not get it to budge more than a centimetre.

The piano was very ___heavy___.

Boris loved his garden more than anything else in the world — he would spend hours after school taking care of his plants.

Boris loved his ....

Doris felt so tired she thought she was going to collapse; she just could not carry on, no matter how hard she tried.

Doris was very ....

Fiona had never felt this happy before — her pulse was racing and there were tears of joy rolling down her face.

Fiona felt very ....

The desert was hotter than the sun, and so dry that even a camel couldn't have survived there for long.

The desert was .... and ....

Leaf me alone — I'm enjoying myself.

Punctuation

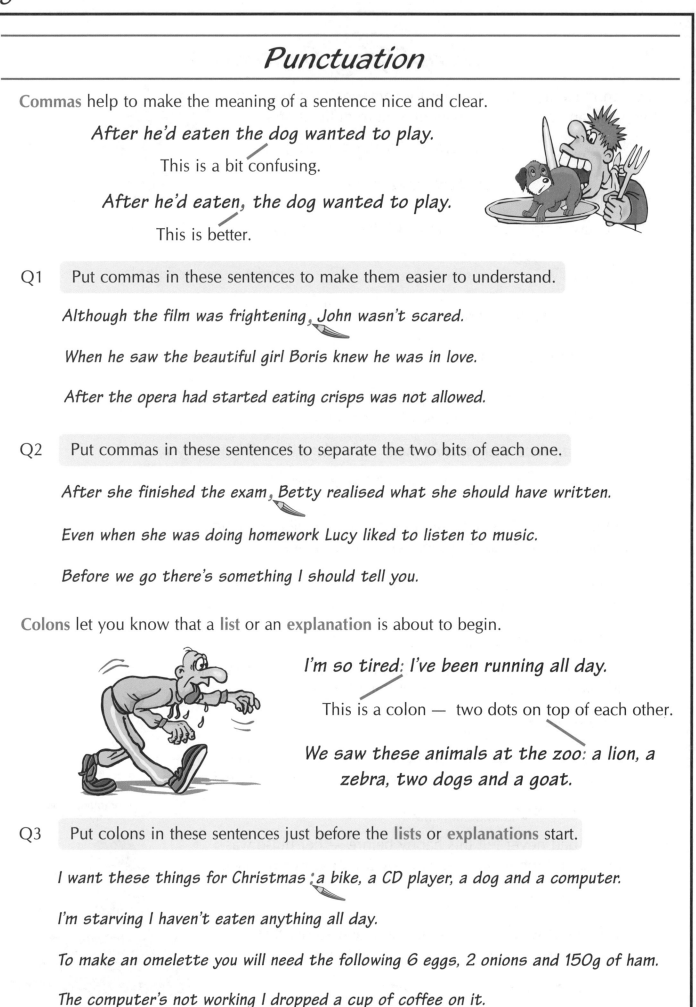

Commas help to make the meaning of a sentence nice and clear.

After he'd eaten the dog wanted to play.

This is a bit confusing.

After he'd eaten, the dog wanted to play.

This is better.

Q1   Put commas in these sentences to make them easier to understand.

Although the film was frightening, John wasn't scared.

When he saw the beautiful girl Boris knew he was in love.

After the opera had started eating crisps was not allowed.

Q2   Put commas in these sentences to separate the two bits of each one.

After she finished the exam, Betty realised what she should have written.

Even when she was doing homework Lucy liked to listen to music.

Before we go there's something I should tell you.

Colons let you know that a **list** or an **explanation** is about to begin.

I'm so tired: I've been running all day.

This is a colon — two dots on top of each other.

We saw these animals at the zoo: a lion, a zebra, two dogs and a goat.

Q3   Put colons in these sentences just before the **lists** or **explanations** start.

I want these things for Christmas : a bike, a CD player, a dog and a computer.

I'm starving I haven't eaten anything all day.

To make an omelette you will need the following 6 eggs, 2 onions and 150g of ham.

The computer's not working I dropped a cup of coffee on it.

Double Negatives

A **double negative** is when you have **two** negative bits in one sentence.

I never said nothing.

'**Never**' is negative...   ...and so is '**nothing**'.

Double negatives cancel each other out — they make the sentence mean the **opposite**.
'I never said nothing' actually means 'I said something'. **Don't** use double negatives.

Q1   Each sentence below has **two** negative bits in it. Draw circles around **both of them**.

Dave (didn't) get (no) dinner.   I never smile at nobody.

I never do no homework.   Our dog doesn't like no strangers.

To make the sentence correct, you need to **change** one of the negative parts.

I didn't say nothing.   → I said nothing.
or
→ I didn't say anything.

Make sure the new sentence makes sense and means what you want it to.
Don't put double negatives in your written work, or you'll lose marks.

Q2   Each of these sentences has a double negative in it.
Change the bit in red so the sentence is correct.

You ain't up to no good, are you?

Nobody's *never* come back from there.   *ever* ....

I can't see *nothing*.   ....

Simon hasn't got *none*.   ....

This film *isn't* no good.   ....

Q3   Tick the box if the sentence is correct, but change
one word if it has a double negative in it.

You're never on time for nothing.   ☐   *anything* ....

I can't do any of these dances.   ☑   ....

I can't get no satisfaction.   ☐   ....

Jim didn't see none of us.   ☐   ....

Verb Tenses

Verb tenses are important because they tell you **when** things happened: past, present or future. Whenever you're writing, remember to stay in the same tense all the way through.

We raced them.   *We race them.*   *We will race them.*

This was in the past.   This is now in the present.   This will happen in the future.

We were racing them.   *We are racing them.*   *We will be racing them.*

Q1   Look at each sentence and write down what tense it is in: past, present or future.

We are going to the moon.   .present.........

They will be going to the moon.   ....

City beat United 5-0 yesterday.   ....

Frederique pushes her sister's pram.   ....

I'm sorry Rex, this isn't the moon. Looks like we'll have to walk.

Q2   Put all of the sentences below into the past tense. There may be two ways to do it.

We are going for a walk.   *Ray is on the rampage.*

We went for a walk.   ....

....

Sandy slurps soggy semolina.   *Barry will be baking buns.*

....

Q3   Here's a paragraph describing a journey in the future. Rewrite it in the present tense.

We will be going on holiday.   *We are going on holiday.*

Dad will be driving, Mum will   ....

be reading the map and   ....

Rita will be singing as loudly   ....

as she can. It will be horrible!   ....

Auxiliary Verbs

Some verbs aren't just single words. They need a **helping verb** (auxiliary verb) as well.

We are sailing.   *It was raining.*   *We could sink.*

'Am/is/are' and 'was/were' are helping verbs. So are 'can' and 'could'.

Other common helping verbs are 'has/have', 'will', 'would', 'be/been/being', 'do' and 'did'.

Q1   Underline the helping verb in each of the sentences below.

The spaceship <u>had</u> arrived late.

She was waiting for hours.

I am staying right here.

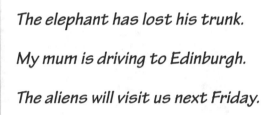

The elephant has lost his trunk.

My mum is driving to Edinburgh.

The aliens will visit us next Friday.

Q2   Add the right helping verb from the list to each sentence so that it makes sense.

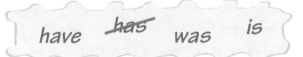

have   ~~has~~   was   is

Rachel <u>has</u> *dressed her car like a cow.*

Michael .... *working late tonight.*

Judy .... *sewing a new quilt all through the winter.*

Alan and Lee .... *flown around the world twice.*

Q3   Rewrite each sentence using the helping verb 'to be' in the present tense. You will need to change the form of the helping verb **and** the main verb.

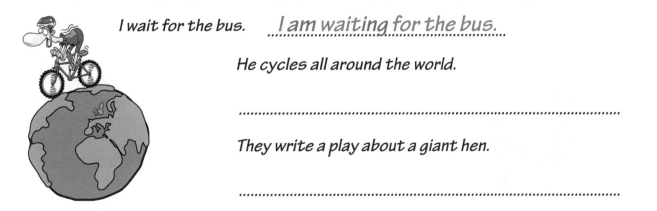

I wait for the bus.   <u>I am waiting for the bus.</u>

He cycles all around the world.

....

They write a play about a giant hen.

....

Synonyms

Synonyms are different words that mean the same thing.
They make your writing much more interesting.

Ben was frightened by the eerie woods.

Ben was scared by the spooky trees.

Ben was afraid of the creepy copse.

Frightened, scared and **afraid** are all synonyms. **Eerie, spooky** and **creepy** are synonyms.

Q1 Look at the words in the middle. There are three groups of synonyms among them. Sort them out into lists, one on each scroll. The first word of each list is done for you.

desolate
....
....
....

uneven
....
....
....

~~uneven~~   rough   knobbly

~~amazing~~   superb

forsaken

~~desolate~~   incredible

forlorn

amazing
....
....
....

Q2 Here is a passage about two famous people.
Replace all the highlighted bits with different words or phrases.

Yesterday, Brian Tweeting asked his girlfriend Jennifer Lee to marry him. Brian, 21, is the main vocalist of the famous group, the Condiment Boyz, while Jennifer is a film star.

The happy couple said they were very excited, as they jetted off to Las Vegas to tie the knot straightaway.

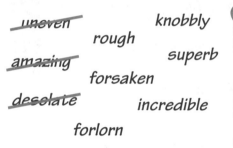

Yesterday, Brian Tweeting proposed to his girlfriend,
Jennifer Lee.
....
....
....
....

Root Words

A lot of words come from one original **root word**.
If you can spot the root word, it can help you work out what the new word means.

*sign*posted   *sign*al

*sign*ed   *sign*ature

All of these words have the root word **sign**. They've all got something to do with signs.

Q1   Pick out the root word in each of these words.

unhelpful — ....*help*....   *personality* — ....

knowledge — ....   *unemotional* — ....

unfaithful — ....   *friendliness* — ....

Q2   Look at the words on the left.
         Find the root word, then draw a line to the related word on the right.

uneasiness   ....*easy*....   *jail*

sleeplessness   ....   *keen*

unenthusiastic   ....   *simple*

forcibly   ....   *rest*

imprisonment   ....   *power*

Root words, perhaps?

Q3   Here is a list of root words. Add prefixes and/or suffixes to make two new words.
         Remember that the spelling can change when you add a suffix.

sense   —   ....*nonsense, sensible*....

cast   —   ....

hero   —   ....

out   —   ....

force   —   ....

Speech

When you write down the **exact words** someone said, you must use **speech marks**.

Cory said, "I don't like banana ketchup."

Q1   Look at the cartoon. Use the speech bubbles to complete the sentences.
Don't forget to put the speech marks in.

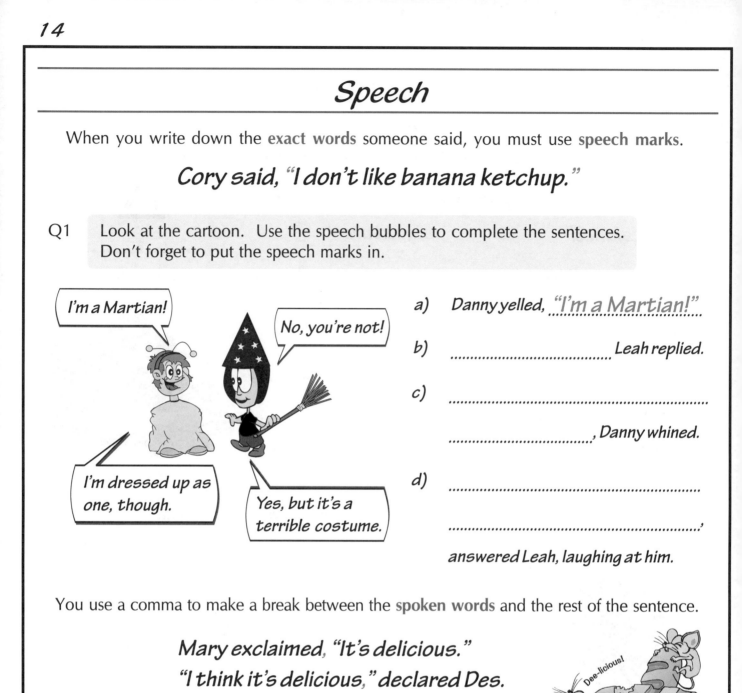

I'm a Martian!

No, you're not!

I'm dressed up as one, though.

Yes, but it's a terrible costume.

a)   Danny yelled, ..."I'm a Martian!"...

b)   .... Leah replied.

c)   ....
..................................., Danny whined.

d)   ....
....,'
answered Leah, laughing at him.

You use a comma to make a break between the **spoken words** and the rest of the sentence.

Mary exclaimed, "It's delicious."
"I think it's delicious," declared Des.

Dee-licious!

Q2   There is one comma missing from every sentence below.
Decide where it should go and put it in.

"I don't like living in this tank," said the little fish.

The chef asked "Has anyone seen my onions?"

Vanessa screamed "Don't let go of the ladder!"

"I can't hold on much longer " Esther replied calmly.

"I'd like to fly to the moon one day " said Neil.

Buzz replied wistfully "Me too, but it's impossible."

Speech

When you're writing down a conversation, start a **new line** every time a new person speaks.

> *"Hello, I'd like to make an appointment," said Mrs Mothball.*
> *"We can do Thursday evening or Friday morning," replied Sandra.*

There's a **new speaker** here, so start a new line.

Q3   Write this conversation out again, adding in the commas and speech marks. Remember to start a new line every time a new person speaks.

I don't think we should pick Harry for the team said Marvin. Why not? asked Jerry. He's always late for practice replied Marvin. That's true agreed Jerry.

"I don't think we should pick Harry for the team," said Marvin.

....

....

....

You can also **report** what somebody said **without** using speech marks.

> *Leah said, "I don't want to play ice hockey." =*
> *Leah said that she didn't want to play ice hockey.*

These aren't the exact words Leah said. You need to use a past tense verb.

Q4   Write these sentences out again using reported speech instead of direct speech.

"I'm going to win the jelly-eating contest!" said Milly.

Milly said that she was going to win the jelly-eating contest.

Ann said, "I can eat a lot more jelly than Milly."

....

"Everybody should eat vegetables instead of jelly," said Mum.

....

Idioms

Idioms are everyday sayings that people use to make their speech more interesting.

I'm a bit under the weather.

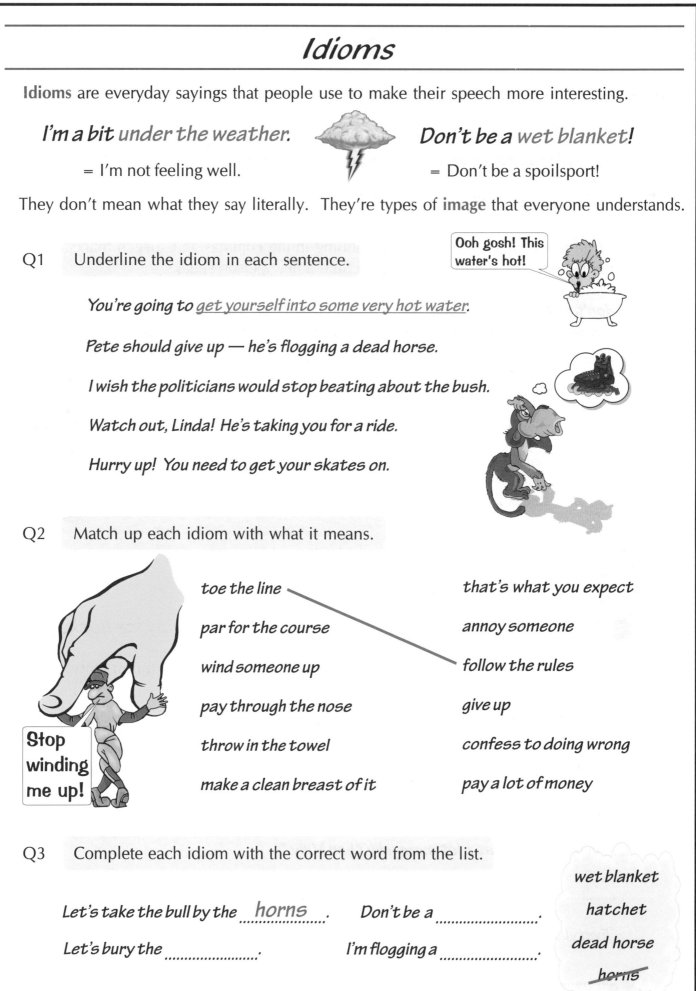

Don't be a wet blanket!

= I'm not feeling well.

= Don't be a spoilsport!

They don't mean what they say literally. They're types of **image** that everyone understands.

Q1 Underline the idiom in each sentence.

Ooh gosh! This water's hot!

You're going to <u>get yourself into some very hot water</u>.

Pete should give up — he's flogging a dead horse.

I wish the politicians would stop beating about the bush.

Watch out, Linda! He's taking you for a ride.

Hurry up! You need to get your skates on.

Q2 Match up each idiom with what it means.

Stop winding me up!

toe the line   that's what you expect

par for the course   annoy someone

wind someone up   follow the rules

pay through the nose   give up

throw in the towel   confess to doing wrong

make a clean breast of it   pay a lot of money

Q3 Complete each idiom with the correct word from the list.

Let's take the bull by the ___horns___ .   Don't be a ....

Let's bury the ....   I'm flogging a ....

wet blanket

hatchet

dead horse

~~horns~~

Idioms

Q4 Look at the short conversations given below, then at the list of idioms on the scroll.
Give the number of the idiom which means the same thing as the words in purple.

"How did it go?" asked Jude.
"I'm quitting!" replied Sadie. "I've had enough." ☐ 2

"What a load of stupid rules!" exclaimed Will.
"Yes, I know, but we have to follow them," sighed Iain. ☐

"Are you sure about this," asked Robbie, "I'm a bit suspicious."
"It'll be fine," answered Andy. ☐

"Never trust a cat like that," said Angie.
"He really fooled me completely", said Marge. ☐

"What are you trying to say, John?" asked Jenny. "Get to the point!"
"I, I, I, I'm-m sc-sc-scared!" he stammered. ☐

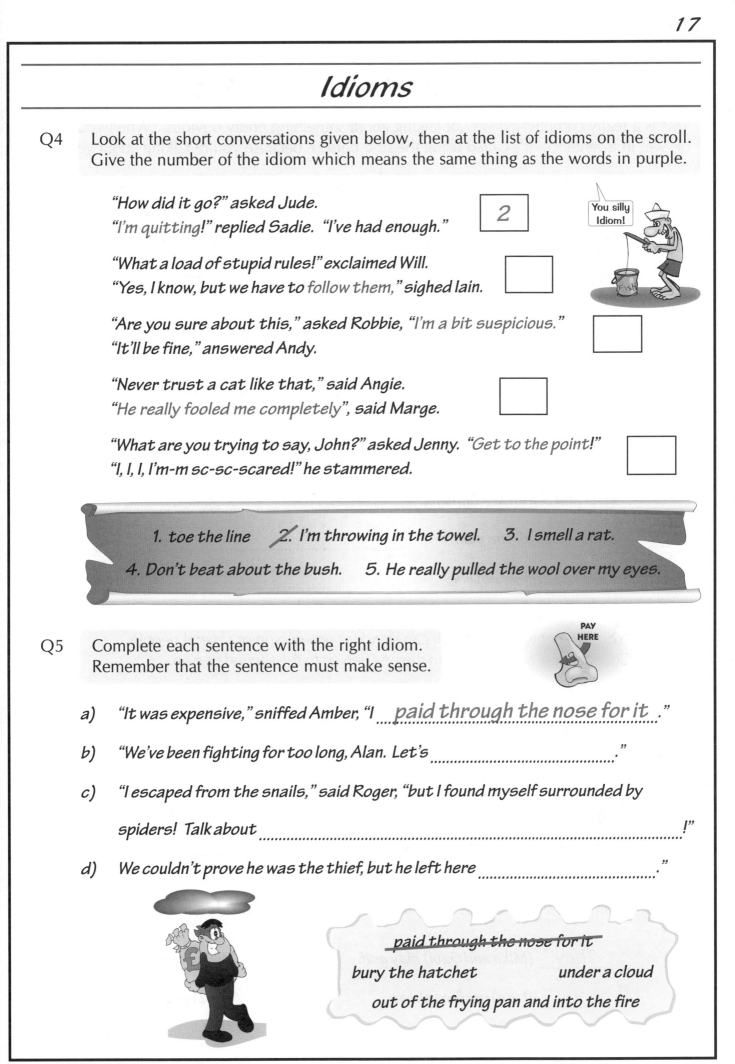

1. toe the line   2. I'm throwing in the towel.   3. I smell a rat.
4. Don't beat about the bush.   5. He really pulled the wool over my eyes.

Q5 Complete each sentence with the right idiom.
Remember that the sentence must make sense.

a) "It was expensive," sniffed Amber, "I ...*paid through the nose for it*...."

b) "We've been fighting for too long, Alan. Let's ...."

c) "I escaped from the snails," said Roger, "but I found myself surrounded by

spiders! Talk about ....!"

d) We couldn't prove he was the thief, but he left here ...."

~~paid through the nose for it~~

bury the hatchet   under a cloud

out of the frying pan and into the fire

First, Second and Third Person

This is a really complicated way of talking about something pretty obvious. When you use 'I' or 'we' in a sentence, it's called using the **first** person, because you're talking about yourself.

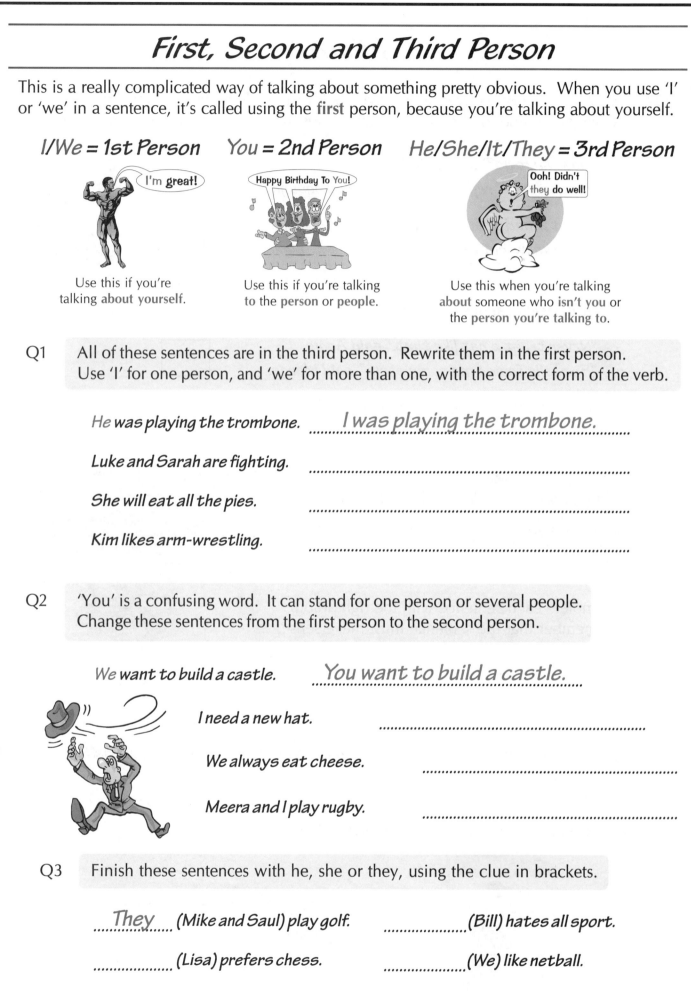

I/We = 1st Person   You = 2nd Person   He/She/It/They = 3rd Person

Use this if you're talking **about yourself**.

Use this if you're talking to the **person** or **people**.

Use this when you're talking **about someone who isn't you** or the **person you're talking to**.

Q1 All of these sentences are in the third person. Rewrite them in the first person. Use 'I' for one person, and 'we' for more than one, with the correct form of the verb.

He *was playing the trombone.* *I was playing the trombone.* ....

Luke and Sarah *are fighting.* ....

She *will eat all the pies.* ....

Kim *likes arm-wrestling.* ....

Q2 'You' is a confusing word. It can stand for one person or several people. Change these sentences from the first person to the second person.

We *want to build a castle.* *You want to build a castle.* ....

I *need a new hat.* ....

We *always eat cheese.* ....

Meera and I *play rugby.* ....

Q3 Finish these sentences with he, she or they, using the clue in brackets.

They .... *(Mike and Saul) play golf.*   .... *(Bill) hates all sport.*

.... *(Lisa) prefers chess.*   .... *(We) like netball.*

First, Second and Third Person

All sentences use the first, second or third person. You need to use the right verb form.

I/we go   *You* go   *He/she/it* goes   *They* go

I am going   *You* are going   *He/she/it* is going   *We/they* are going

These forms are all in the present tense. Make sure you use the right one with each person.

Q4   Fill in the gaps with the right present tense form from the list.

> ~~buy~~   Are you going
> is buying   goes
> eats   am eating

We ......*buy*...... all our shopping at the market.

He .... so much food that he makes himself sick.

This week, I .... only spinach and baked bean soup.

Janet never .... to the hairdresser.

.... to the match on Saturday?

Larry's Mum .... him a new troll.

Q5   Use each set of words to make up a sentence. You may need to add extra words. Put the verb into the right present tense form so the sentence makes sense.

We, go, Hawaii, water-skiing, next week

...We are going water-skiing in Hawaii next week....

Darren, go, tap-dancing, London, every evening.

....

I, wait, last bus home.

....

You, wear, new jacket, today.

....

Rhymes

Two different words **rhyme** when they end with the same **sounds**. All these words rhyme.

pain rhymes with mane and lane

The **last part** of each word sounds the same when you say it out loud.

Q1   Draw lines to join up the rhyming words in this poem.

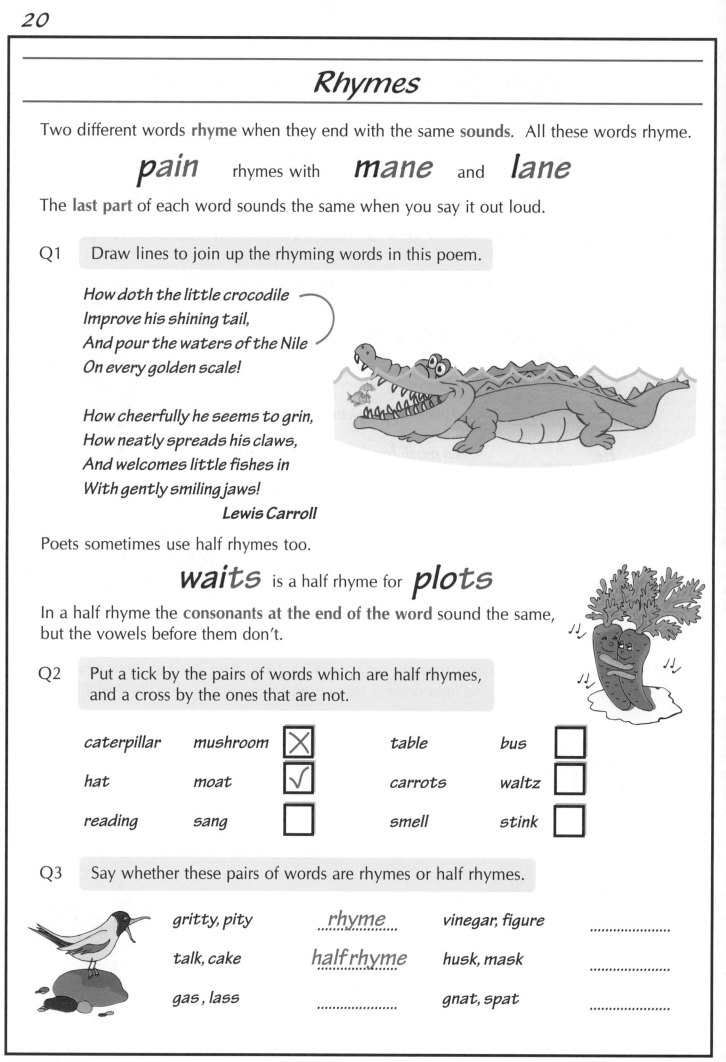

How doth the little crocodile
Improve his shining tail,
And pour the waters of the Nile
On every golden scale!

How cheerfully he seems to grin,
How neatly spreads his claws,
And welcomes little fishes in
With gently smiling jaws!
                    Lewis Carroll

Poets sometimes use half rhymes too.

waits is a half rhyme for plots

In a half rhyme the **consonants at the end of the word** sound the same, but the vowels before them don't.

Q2   Put a tick by the pairs of words which are half rhymes, and a cross by the ones that are not.

caterpillar	mushroom	☒	table	bus	☐
hat	moat	✓	carrots	waltz	☐
reading	sang	☐	smell	stink	☐

Q3   Say whether these pairs of words are rhymes or half rhymes.

gritty, pity	_rhyme_	vinegar, figure	....
talk, cake	_half rhyme_	husk, mask	....
gas, lass	....	gnat, spat	....

Rhymes

In poetry rhyming words are usually put at the **end** of a line,
but sometimes two rhyming words are put on the **same line**.

Hey-diddle-diddle, the cat and the fiddle,

The cow jumped over the moon.

This is called an **internal rhyme**.

Q4   Circle the internal rhymes in these verses.
Remember that it's not a rhyme if the two words are the same.

Who are you calling fat and stout?

The worms crawl out and the worms crawl in,
The ones that crawl in are lean and thin,
The ones that crawl out are fat and stout,
Be merry, my friends, be merry.

'I see by your outfit that you are a cowboy'—
These words did he say as I boldly stepped by,
'Come sit down beside me and hear my sad story;
I'm shot in the breast and I know I must die.'

Another trick writers use is starting several words with the **same sound**.

The sea sighed and seethed over the shingly shore.

This is called **alliteration**. It makes the words sound as though they belong together.

Q5   Write down two words which start with the same letter as each of these words.
Then write down a word which rhymes, and a word which half rhymes.

	trees	**space**	**sunny**
alliterating words	towers	....	....
	twisted	....	....
rhyming word	breeze	....	....
half rhyming word	grows	....	....

Adverbs about Talking

Stories get **boring** if you write 'he said' and 'she said' all the time.

"They're going to free the bears,"Kerry said. ⬅ This is a bit **boring**.

It's a lot more interesting if you **don't** use 'said' all the time.
You can also use **adverbs** to give a better description of how people speak.

"They're going to free the bears,"Kerry shouted triumphantly.

The sentence is much more exciting now, because you can imagine how Kerry spoke.

Q1   Fit one of the adverbs from the blob into each sentence.

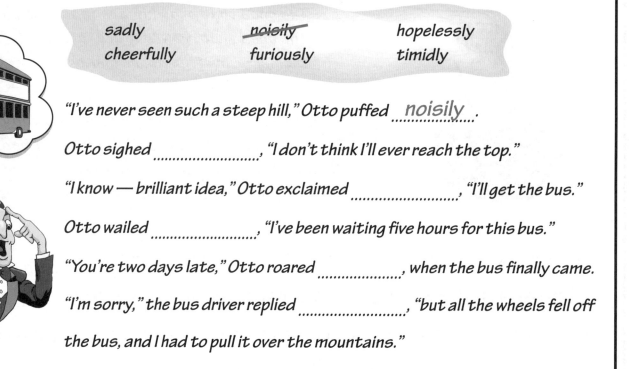

sadly   ~~noisily~~   hopelessly

cheerfully   furiously   timidly

"I've never seen such a steep hill,"Otto puffed __noisily__ .

Otto sighed _____, "I don't think I'll ever reach the top."

"I know — brilliant idea,"Otto exclaimed _____, "I'll get the bus."

Otto wailed _____, "I've been waiting five hours for this bus."

"You're two days late,"Otto roared _____, when the bus finally came.

"I'm sorry,"the bus driver replied _____, "but all the wheels fell off

the bus, and I had to pull it over the mountains."

Q2   Finish off these sentences without using the word 'said'.
Use a different adverb in each sentence to describe the way the words are spoken.

"Earlier today a dinosaur fell on Parliament,"the newsreader __announced calmly__ .

"Would you like ice cream with that, Sir?" _____ the waitress _____ .

"That's City's seventh goal today,"the commentator _____ _____ .

"Stop messing around!"the teacher _____ _____ .

"I'm not doing anything,"Angelica _____ _____ .

Word Order

In most sentences there are some words which are **more important** than others.

The Jones's caravan rolled slowly back down the hill.
The caravan rolled down the hill.

The sentence still **makes sense** when you leave out the less important words.

Q1   Write these sentences again, leaving out any words that are not very important.

The blue dog barked at the skinny cat.

.....*The dog barked at the cat.*.....

My favourite aunt gave me a huge bar of chocolate.

....

Ferocious tigers and gentle gibbons live in the deep lush forests of Borneo.

....

You can also change the order of the words in a sentence.

The caveman chased the mammoth on Saturday.
The mammoth chased the caveman on Saturday.
On Saturday, the mammoth chased the caveman.

The same words mean something totally different now.

Here the order has changed but the meaning is the same.

Q2   Change the order of the words to make new sentences.

My uncle put a huge chicken on the barbecue.

.....*A huge chicken put my uncle on the barbecue.*.....

The spaceship landed on Mars.

....

The fisherman caught a gigantic flounder.

....

Writing Instructions

Instructions tell you **how to** do something. They are written in a special way.

Remove all packaging.

Cook in the oven at 190 °C.

You **don't** write 'you remove', or 'you have to remove', just '**remove**'.

Q1   Using the words in the box fill in the blanks in these instructions.

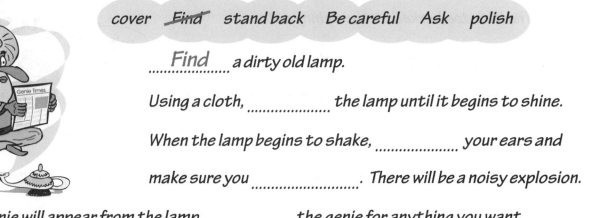

cover   ~~Find~~   stand back   Be careful   Ask   polish

........Find........ *a dirty old lamp.*

Using a cloth, ... *the lamp until it begins to shine.*

When the lamp begins to shake, ... *your ears and*

make sure you .... *. There will be a noisy explosion.*

A genie will appear from the lamp. .... *the genie for anything you want.*

........................! *I once asked for a tonne of chocolate, and it landed right on top of me.*

Q2   Write instructions explaining how to brush your teeth. Imagine that the person who is going to read your instructions has never brushed their teeth before (yuck!).

Pick up a toothbrush. Make sure it is yours.

....

....

....

....

....

....

....

....

Saying What's Happened

When you talk or write about something that has **already happened** you use the **past tense**.

I spilt milk all over the kitchen floor.
Luckily the dog licked it all up before Mum found out.

Q1   Circle the words in the past tense in these sentences.

In AD 43 the Roman Emperor Claudius (conquers / conquered) Britain.

Lots of Roman soldiers (were / are) sent to live in Britain.

The soldiers (built / build) long straight roads.

These roads (joined / join) the main towns together.

They (make / made) it easier for the soldiers to travel round the country.

The Caledonians, people from the north of Britain, (attack / attacked) the Romans.

The Emperor Hadrian (ordered / orders) a huge wall to be built to keep them out.

Q2   Write these sentences out again, putting the purple words into the past tense.

I (go) ___went___ to Rome on holiday. From my room I

(can) .... see the stadium, which the Romans (call)

.... the Colosseum, and the Forum, which (is) ....

the Roman city centre. The Romans (use) .... white

marble for the important buildings. These buildings all (have)

.... columns along the front.

The Roman men (wear) .... outfits called togas.

They (make) .... them from big woollen sheets, and

(fasten) .... them with metal pins.

Spelling Rules

You can add the word '**full**' to some words to make new words.

mouth + full ➡ **mouthful**

You always leave off the last **l**.

Q1 Add '**full**' to make new words. Don't forget to leave off the last **l**.

care + full	_careful_	harm + full	....
play + full	....	hope + full	....
cheer + full	....	use + full	....
tear + full	....	spoon + full	....
thank + full	....	power + full	....

When the letter **c** comes in front of most letters it makes a hard sound like **k**. But when it comes in front of an **i** or an **e** it makes a soft sound like **s**.

cauliflower   city   cell
hard sound   soft sound   soft sound

Q2 Look at these words and say them out loud.
Write down '**hard**', or '**soft**' to describe the sound the first **c** makes.

a hard cup of coffee

a squishy soft centipede

clap	_hard_	circle	....
ceiling	_soft_	citizen	....
cartoon	....	cod	....
circus	....	cinema	....
centimetre	....	crayon	....
crumb	....	cactus	....

Suffixes

The suffixes, or endings, of these words are **spelt differently**, but they **sound** the same.

station   mansion   musician

Words with the suffix **-sian** sound slightly different.
It's often the ending on words that tell you where somebody is **from**.

Friesian   Persian

Words which describe a person's job, or where they're from **always** end **-an**, **never -on**.

electrician   dietician

Q1   Draw lines to match these words with the endings on the right.

attention

tension

television

fraction

optician

extension

Indonesian

action

-cian
-sian
-sion
-tion

Q2   All these words have the wrong suffix.
Write them out again with the right suffix below.

educacian	illustrasion	politision
education	....	....
Asion	magition	televician
....	....	....
concentrasian	decician	temptacian
....	....	....

Double Letters

Say these words out loud. They **don't** sound the same.

robed   *robbed*

The **o** in **robbed** is very short compared to the **o** in **robed**.
When you add suffixes to a word with a short vowel, the last letter is **doubled**.

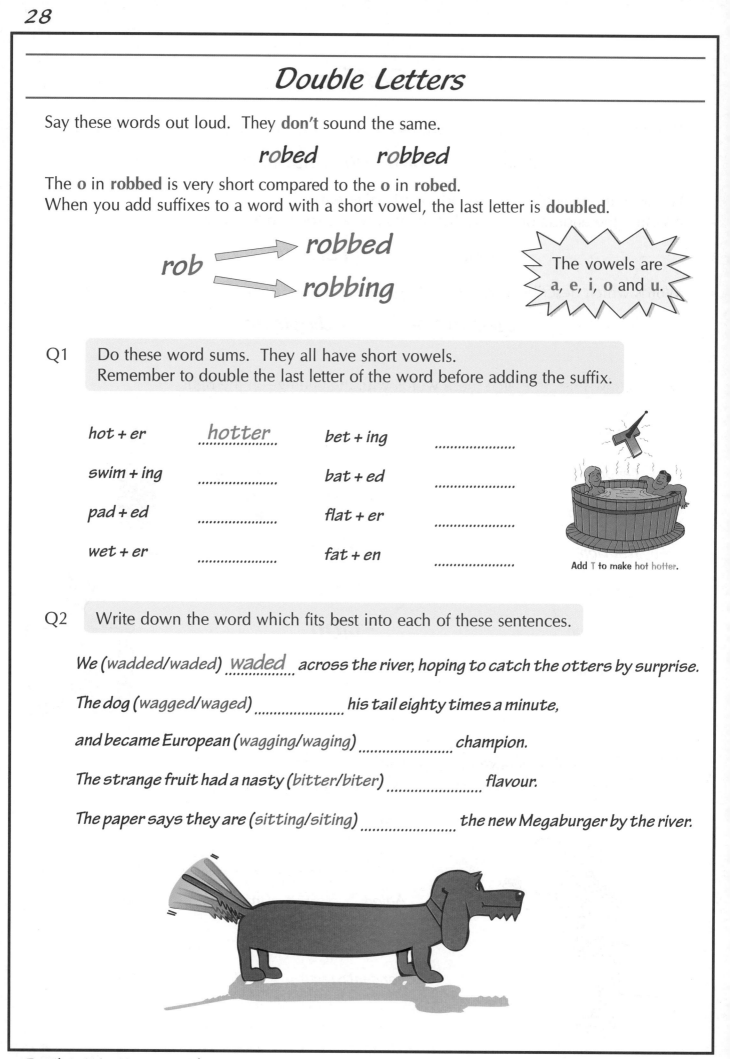

rob → *robbed*
rob → *robbing*

The vowels are
a, e, i, o and **u**.

Q1   Do these word sums. They all have short vowels.
Remember to double the last letter of the word before adding the suffix.

hot + er   *hotter*   bet + ing   ....

swim + ing   ....   bat + ed   ....

pad + ed   ....   flat + er   ....

wet + er   ....   fat + en   ....

Add T to make hot hotter.

Q2   Write down the word which fits best into each of these sentences.

We (*wadded/waded*) *waded* across the river, hoping to catch the otters by surprise.

The dog (*wagged/waged*) .... his tail eighty times a minute,

and became European (*wagging/waging*) .... champion.

The strange fruit had a nasty (*bitter/biter*) .... flavour.

The paper says they are (*sitting/siting*) .... the new Megaburger by the river.

Double Letters

These words all have a **long vowel sound**.
If the vowel is long, the letter afterwards **doesn't double** — you just add the ending.

peel + ed ➡ peeled   wait + er ➡ waiter

Words like '**pick**' already have **two consonants** at the end of the word. Just add the ending.

pick + ing ➡ picking

Q3   Do these word sums. Remember you only need to double the last letter
     when the vowel sound in the middle of the word is **short** with **one** consonant.

tick + ed   ...ticked...   mat + ed   ....   dig + er   ....

pain + ed   ....   call + er   ....   build + er   ....

feel + ing   ....   smell + ing   ....

wreck + ed   ....   talk + ed   ....

Q4   Finish off the incomplete words in these sentences.
     Make sure you double the last letter when you need to.

Jemima is taller than Maisie.

Dad gril.......... the fish fingers, but I usually fry them.

She was astonished. "I don't believe it," she exclaim..........?

I can't draw a straight line. Can I borrow your rul..........?

The workmen pick.......... it up and hurl.......... it over the fence.

The sea was so cold that we just dip.......... our toes into the water.

I just couldn't get the pieces straight. I thought I'd never get them lin.......... up.

Four Kinds of Noun

Words which name **people**, **animals**, **places** and **things** are called nouns.
These three nouns are **common nouns**.

town   river   hippopotamus

Common nouns are the names of **kinds of things**.
A hippopotamus is one **kind** of animal.   A town is one **kind** of place where people live.

Q1   Circle all the words which are **nouns**.

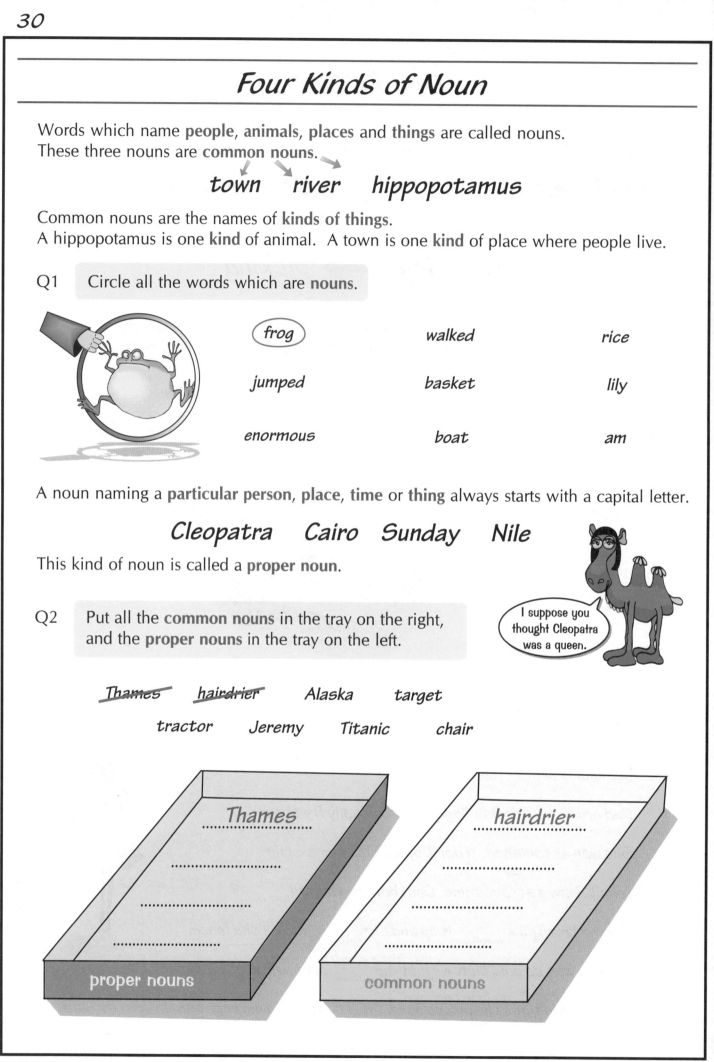

frog   walked   rice

jumped   basket   lily

enormous   boat   am

A noun naming a **particular person**, **place**, **time** or **thing** always starts with a capital letter.

Cleopatra   Cairo   Sunday   Nile

This kind of noun is called a **proper noun**.

I suppose you thought Cleopatra was a queen.

Q2   Put all the **common nouns** in the tray on the right, and the **proper nouns** in the tray on the left.

~~Thames~~   ~~hairdrier~~   Alaska   target

tractor   Jeremy   Titanic   chair

Thames
....
....
....

hairdrier
....
....
....

proper nouns   **common nouns**

Four Kinds of Noun

There are some nouns which are used specially to talk about **groups of things**.

a gaggle of geese
a swarm of bees

A noun used for talking about groups of things is called a **collective noun**.

Q3   Draw lines to match the **collective nouns** with the words on the right.

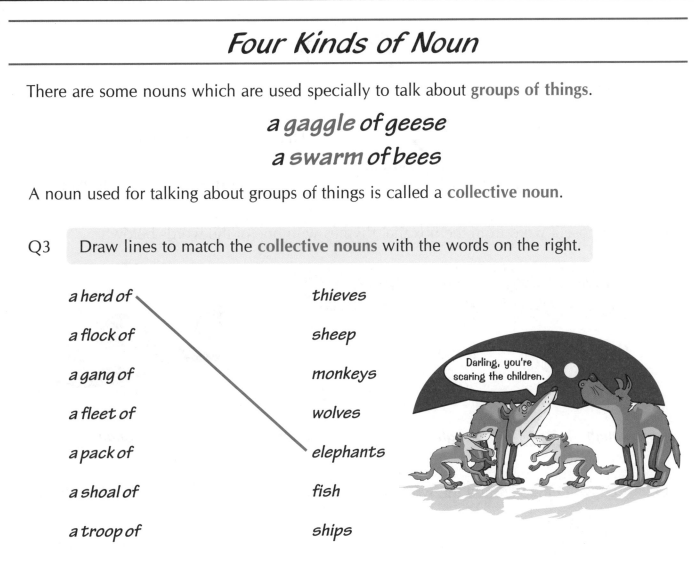

a herd of   thieves

a flock of   sheep

a gang of   monkeys

a fleet of   wolves

a pack of   elephants

a shoal of   fish

a troop of   ships

Some nouns describe things which you can't actually **see**, **hear**, **smell**, **touch** or **taste**.

happiness   excitement

These nouns are called **abstract nouns**.

Q4   Circle the abstract nouns in this story. There are six altogether.

As the plane reached 4, 000 metres Anton was filled with (dread.)

The door creaked open, and fear turned his limbs to jelly. "This is no

time for cowardice," Anton told himself, and leapt out. As he hurtled

towards the airfield, he was surprised to find he was having fun. He

tugged the parachute cord, and suddenly there was peace and quiet.

"Lovely afternoon," called a passing pigeon.

Spelling

Some words end with the same group of letters, but you say them in very different ways.

here   *there*

Both these words end in **-ere** — but they sound very different.

Here rhymes with **near**...

...but **there** rhymes with **hair**.

Q1 Choose a word from the box that rhymes with one of the words below.

> dude   tough   ~~near~~   ~~hair~~   mud
> blow   good   off   new

Watch the catch.

here *near*   there *hair*

wood ....   food ....   blood ....

cough ....   rough ....   though ....   through ....

Q2 Draw a circle around the word in each group that **doesn't** rhyme with the others.

Phil feels ill.

clear   near   (pear)   watch   catch   scratch

wool   cool   school   rough   tough   though

sew   knew   new   love   prove   glove

Q3 Complete the words in the sentences with the correct endings from the box. You need to use the same ending for both words in each sentence.

> -ew   -oot   ~~-ead~~   -ork

I can't r *ead* this recipe for making br *ead* .

My f .... is too big to get into this b ....

The button on my n .... jacket is missing so I need to s .... another one on.

Put that knife and f .... on the table as Sam will be home from w .... soon.

Antonyms

Antonym is another word for **opposite**.

'Short' is an antonym of 'tall'.   *'Young' is an antonym of 'old'.*

Q1 Join up these words to their antonyms.

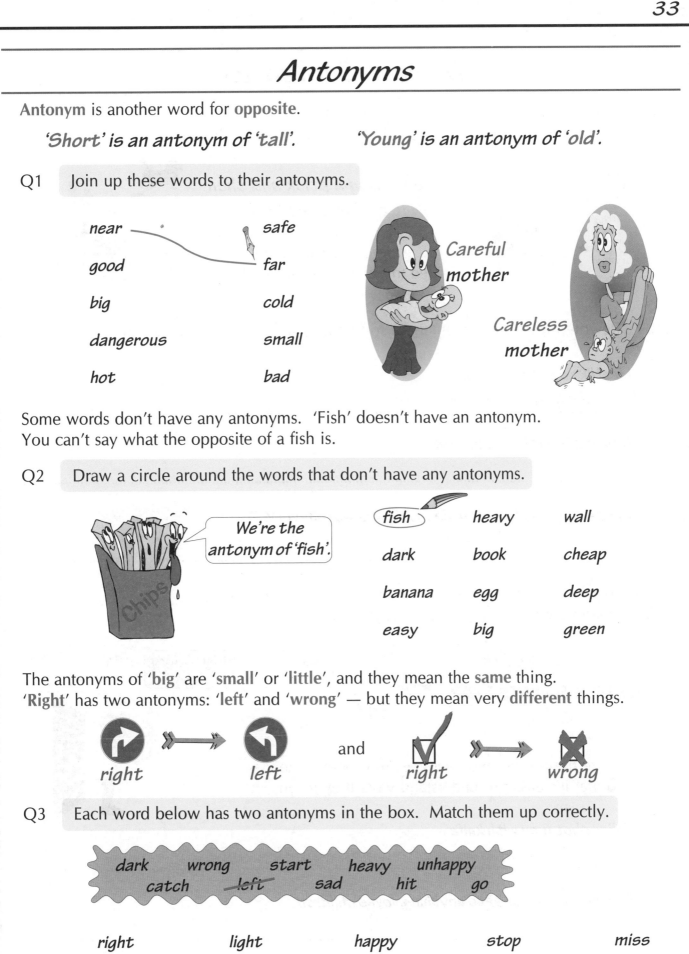

near   safe

good   far

big   cold

dangerous   small

hot   bad

Careful mother

Careless mother

Some words don't have any antonyms. 'Fish' doesn't have an antonym.
You can't say what the opposite of a fish is.

Q2 Draw a circle around the words that don't have any antonyms.

We're the antonym of 'fish'.

fish	heavy	wall
dark	book	cheap
banana	egg	deep
easy	big	green

The antonyms of '**big**' are '**small**' or '**little**', and they mean the **same** thing.
'**Right**' has two antonyms: '**left**' and '**wrong**' — but they mean very **different** things.

right → left   and   right → wrong

Q3 Each word below has two antonyms in the box. Match them up correctly.

dark   wrong   start   heavy   unhappy
catch   left   sad   hit   go

right   light   happy   stop   miss
left
....

....

Unclear Sentences

Sometimes a sentence isn't as **clear** as you think.
Always make sure your sentences say clearly what you want them to say.

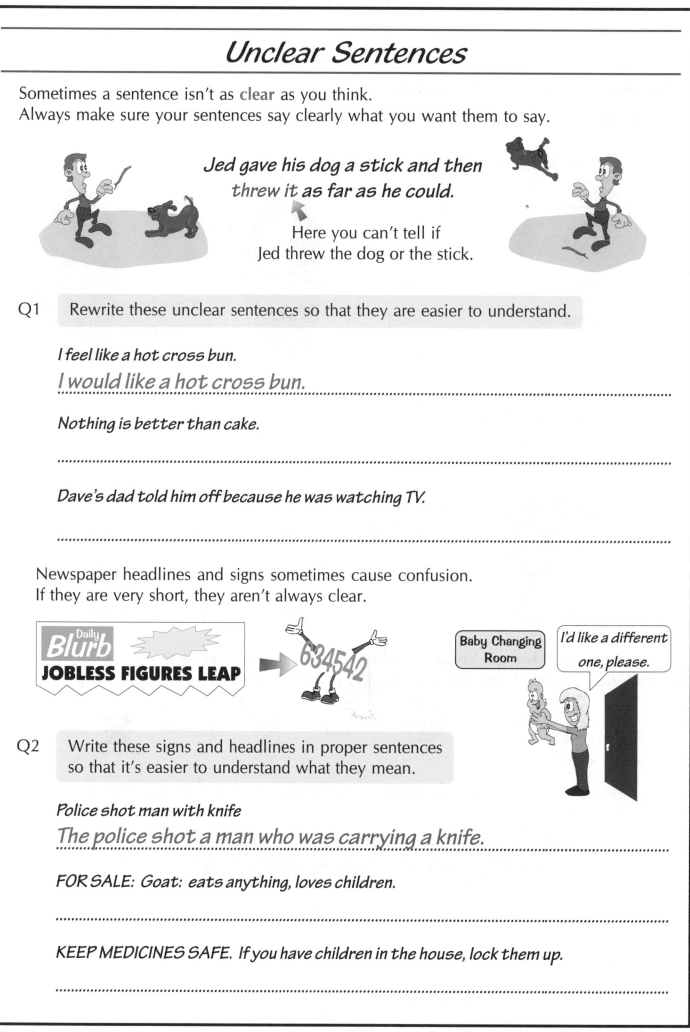

Jed gave his dog a stick and then threw it as far as he could.

Here you can't tell if
Jed threw the dog or the stick.

Q1   Rewrite these unclear sentences so that they are easier to understand.

I feel like a hot cross bun.
I would like a hot cross bun.
....

Nothing is better than cake.

....

Dave's dad told him off because he was watching TV.

....

Newspaper headlines and signs sometimes cause confusion.
If they are very short, they aren't always clear.

Daily **Blurb**
JOBLESS FIGURES LEAP
634542

Baby Changing Room

I'd like a different one, please.

Q2   Write these signs and headlines in proper sentences
so that it's easier to understand what they mean.

Police shot man with knife
The police shot a man who was carrying a knife.
....

FOR SALE: Goat: eats anything, loves children.

....

KEEP MEDICINES SAFE. If you have children in the house, lock them up.

....

Onomatopoeia

Onomatopoeia is when a word **sounds** like what it means.

Whole phrases can also be onomatopoeic, like this bit of a poem.

And the murmur of innumerable bees.

Q1 Match up each onomatopoeic word with the picture that fits it best.

cockadoodledoo [C]

pop [ ]

cuckoo [ ]

sizzle [ ]

Q2 Fill in the gaps in each sentence with the best onomatopoeic word below.

popped   creaked   fizzed   ~~croak~~   coughing

The frog started to ..... *croak* ..... when it saw the man approaching.

The cork .... out and lemonade .... everywhere.

The stairs .... as Melanie climbed them.

Jack couldn't stop .... when he was ill in bed with the flu.

Q3 Invent an onomatopoeic word for each of the gaps in these sentences.

Harry jumped into the pool with a loud ..... *ploosh* .....

Jennie .... her spaghetti.

Leroy fell out of bed with a ....

Bert's cat made a loud .... when it tried to eat the lawnmower cable.

Homophones

Homophones are words that sound the same but are spelt differently and mean different things.

He ate eight pies.

The words '**ate**' and '**eight**' are homophones.

Q1 Underline the right word to complete each sentence below.

Do me a favour and go to the baker's to get some (bred / (bread)).

I fancy some cheese on the pizza I've ordered so I'll (grate / great) some now.

The jockey pulled on the (rains / reigns / reins) to get the horse to stop.

Q2 Choose a pair of homophones from the box to fill in the gaps in these sentences.

board	bored
knot	not
deer	dear
~~maid~~	~~made~~

Where's the   maid   ? She hasn't   made   the beds.

My .... friend Rod saw four .... at the zoo.

I'm .... — I want to play a .... game.

Who tied this .... ? It is .... tight enough.

Q3 Look at this paragraph. Someone has written all the wrong homophones. Replace each word in red with the correct homophone so it makes sense.

Unfortunately, I can't fined

that wonderful new book witch

I said I wood lend two Boris

Ackerman, the baker's sun.

Have you scene it recently? I no

I had it last Monday.

fined	find
witch	....
wood	....
two	....
sun	....
scene	....
no	....

Metaphors

Metaphors are images in which you say a person, animal or thing **is** something else. They aren't really true — but they give you an idea what the thing is like.

He was a rock in defence.

It means he was solid, like a rock.

Metaphors are stronger than **similes**, which use the words *like* or *as*.

His hands felt like sandpaper. ◄ This is a simile.

Q1 Write **M** in the box if the sentence is a metaphor, but write **S** if it's a simile.

He could run like lightning when he had to. ☑ S

That man is an absolute diamond. ☐

His fists were like an anvil. ☐

My brother is an animal at mealtimes. ☐

Q2 Turn these similes into metaphors.

The moon was like a giant white dinner plate in the sky.
The moon was a giant white dinner plate in the sky.

She is like a spoilt princess.

....

The tree was like a scarecrow in the moonlight.

....

Q3 Choose the best word to complete these metaphors.

    sunshine   angel   ~~turkey~~

That new film is a complete ......turkey........ .

You are the .... *that lights up my day.*

My brother is a little .... *— he's always helping around the house.*

Pronouns

You use pronouns **instead** of nouns to avoid using the same words again and again.

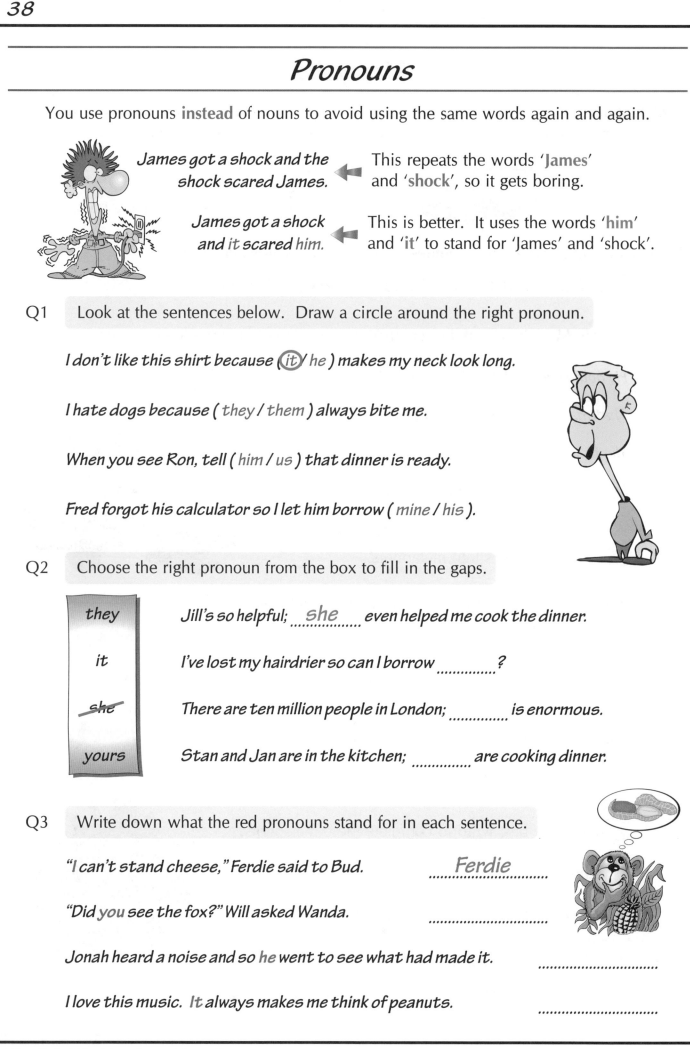

James got a shock and the shock scared James. ← This repeats the words '**James**' and '**shock**', so it gets boring.

James got a shock and *it* scared him. ← This is better. It uses the words '**him**' and '**it**' to stand for 'James' and 'shock'.

Q1   Look at the sentences below. Draw a circle around the right pronoun.

I don't like this shirt because (it / he) makes my neck look long.

I hate dogs because (they / them) always bite me.

When you see Ron, tell (him / us) that dinner is ready.

Fred forgot his calculator so I let him borrow (mine / his).

Q2   Choose the right pronoun from the box to fill in the gaps.

they
it
~~she~~
yours

Jill's so helpful; _she_ even helped me cook the dinner.

I've lost my hairdrier so can I borrow _____?

There are ten million people in London; _____ is enormous.

Stan and Jan are in the kitchen; _____ are cooking dinner.

Q3   Write down what the red pronouns stand for in each sentence.

"I can't stand cheese," Ferdie said to Bud.   _Ferdie_

"Did you see the fox?" Will asked Wanda.   ....

Jonah heard a noise and so he went to see what had made it.   ....

I love this music. It always makes me think of peanuts.   ....

Words Ending in '-e'

If you add a suffix to a word ending in -e, sometimes the -e disappears.
It all depends on the suffix.

hope + ing ➡ hoping

With -ing, the -e **disappears**. There's no 'e' in hoping.

hope + ful ➡ hopeful

If the first letter of the suffix is a **consonant**, the -e **stays**.

> The letters **a**, **e**, **i**, **o** and **u** are *vowels*. Everything else is a *consonant*.

Q1 Do these word sums to make new words.

use	+	less	=	*useless*	make	+	ing	=	....
skate	+	ing	=	....	hope	+	less	=	....
hope	+	ful	=	....	drive	+	ing	=	....
slope	+	ing	=	....	life	+	less	=	....

Q2 Underline the right spelling of each word.

What are you (smiling / smileing) about?

The sun's (rising / riseing) so we'd better get off.

Mick insisted he was only (jokeing / joking), but

   Rick still didn't find it funny.

"Abe's not (comeing / coming) this evening," said Mike. "He's trapped under a piano."

Q3 Draw a circle around each of the mistakes in these sentences and write the proper spelling of each word in the space.

Lilly's completly lifeless in the morning. ....*completely*........

Mum's bakeing a birthday cake for Sam. ....

This yoghurt has no flavour — it's tastless. ....

Doug's decorateing the kitchen this week. ....

Apostrophes

An **apostrophe** + 's' shows that something **belongs to** someone.

Q1 Put an apostrophe in the right place in each sentence.

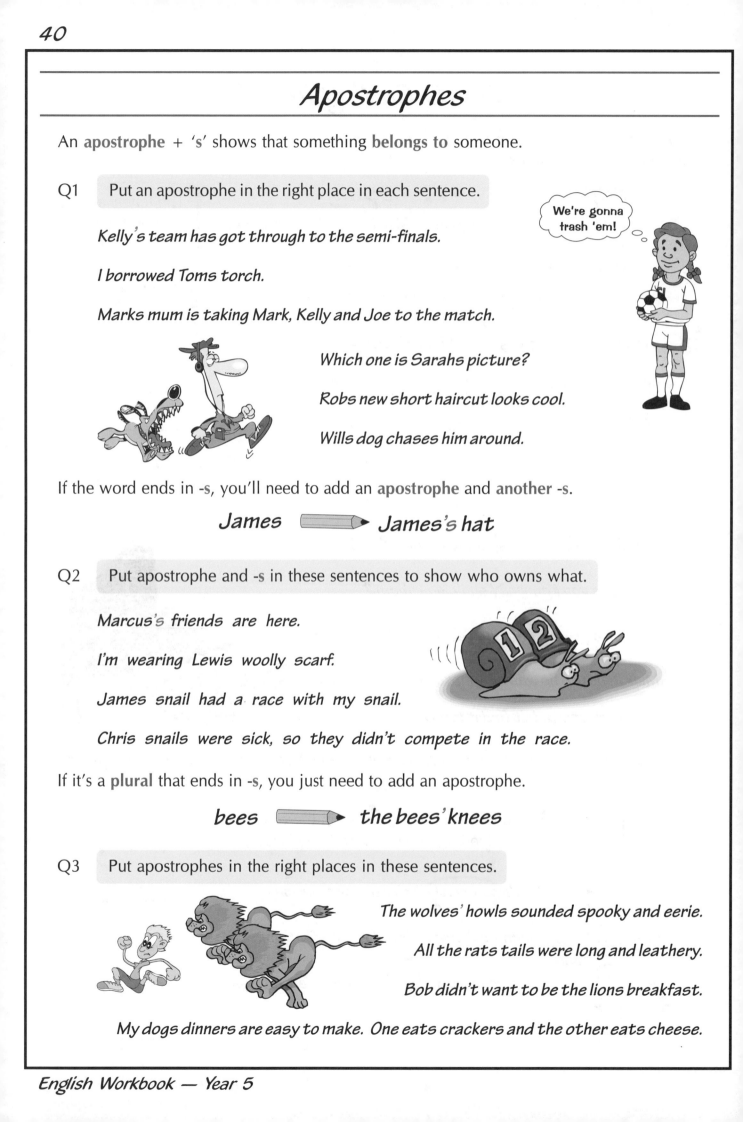

Kelly's team has got through to the semi-finals.

I borrowed Toms torch.

Marks mum is taking Mark, Kelly and Joe to the match.

Which one is Sarahs picture?

Robs new short haircut looks cool.

Wills dog chases him around.

If the word ends in **-s**, you'll need to add an **apostrophe** and **another -s**.

James ➡ James's hat

Q2 Put apostrophe and **-s** in these sentences to show who owns what.

Marcus's friends are here.

I'm wearing Lewis woolly scarf.

James snail had a race with my snail.

Chris snails were sick, so they didn't compete in the race.

If it's a **plural** that ends in **-s**, you just need to add an apostrophe.

bees ➡ the bees' knees

Q3 Put apostrophes in the right places in these sentences.

The wolves' howls sounded spooky and eerie.

All the rats tails were long and leathery.

Bob didn't want to be the lions breakfast.

My dogs dinners are easy to make. One eats crackers and the other eats cheese.

Apostrophes

Apostrophes are also used to write short forms of words, like **isn't** and **they're**.
The **apostrophe** goes in place of the **letters** that are **missed out**.

they are  *they're*

Q4 Rewrite each of these sentences using **short forms** of words wherever you can.

Do not tell Katy what I have got for her birthday. It is meant to be a surprise.

Don't tell Katy what I've got for her birthday.

It's meant to be a surprise.

I cannot tell what I am supposed to do.

....

We are going to be late if you do not hurry up.

....

The film was not very good.

....

If you have watched the film you will know why I did not like it.

....

It's is short for **it is or it has**. **Its** means **belonging** to **it** — **its** has **no apostrophe**.

Q5 Look at each sentence and work out if you should use **its** or **it's**.
Underline the correct one.

(It's / Its) going to be a lovely day.

When I let the dog off (it's / its) lead, it went crazy.

(It's / Its) running around the park at a hundred miles an hour.

This milk's been out so long that (it's / its) gone off.

The school is changing (it's / its) uniform policy so we can dress up as animals.

Unstressed Vowels

A vowel is **unstressed** when it's **not** pronounced with a strong sound.
Unstressed vowels all tend to sound the **same**, so you have to be careful with **spellings**.

The 'a' in company sounds more like 'uh'.
It doesn't sound like the 'a' in **pan**.

company

The 'ai' in curtain sounds more like 'uh'.
It doesn't sound like the 'ai' in **pain**.

curtain

Q1 Underline the unstressed vowels in these words.

elephant   strengthen

interesting   even

metal   cauldron

Interesting... a metal strengthening potion.

I'm confused.

Q2 Fill in the missing vowel in these words.

int _e_ rest   cat......gories   const.......ntly

cat.....logue   vari.....ty   cat.....rpillar

comm......n   pers....nal

pati.....nt   fortun.....tely

tot......lly   spani.....l

Q3 Underline the correct spellings.

Adders are (poisanus / poisonous) snakes.

(Elephunts / Elephants) have got (enormous / enormus) ears.

(Novelists / Novalists) write stories for a living.

I'll try to (discribe / describe) what I saw.

They had the most amazing (varieties / variaties) of jam.

Dialect Words

People speak **differently** in different parts of the country. They have different accents, and sometimes even different words. These words are called **dialect words**.

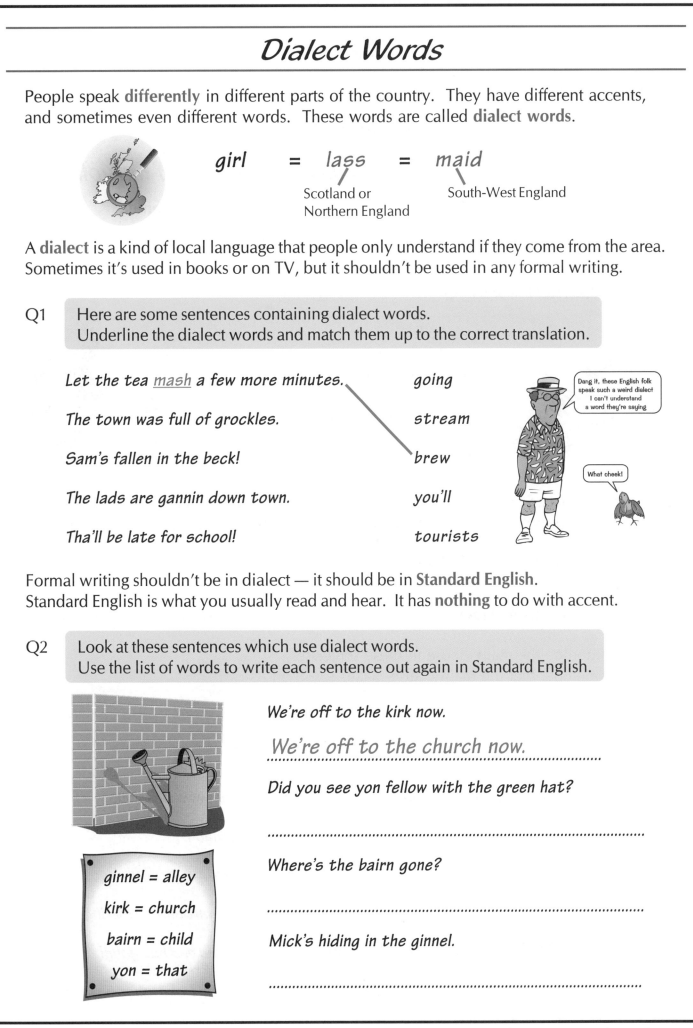

girl = *lass* = *maid*

Scotland or
Northern England

South-West England

A **dialect** is a kind of local language that people only understand if they come from the area. Sometimes it's used in books or on TV, but it shouldn't be used in any formal writing.

Q1 Here are some sentences containing dialect words.
Underline the dialect words and match them up to the correct translation.

Let the tea <u>mash</u> a few more minutes.   going

The town was full of grockles.   stream

Sam's fallen in the beck!   brew

The lads are gannin down town.   you'll

Tha'll be late for school!   tourists

Dang it, these English folk speak such a weird dialect I can't understand a word they're saying

What cheek!

Formal writing shouldn't be in dialect — it should be in **Standard English**.
Standard English is what you usually read and hear. It has **nothing** to do with accent.

Q2 Look at these sentences which use dialect words.
Use the list of words to write each sentence out again in Standard English.

We're off to the kirk now.

We're off to the church now.
....

Did you see yon fellow with the green hat?

....

Where's the bairn gone?

....

Mick's hiding in the ginnel.

....

ginnel = alley
kirk = church
bairn = child
yon = that

Clauses

A **clause** is any bit of a sentence with a **verb**.

Gareth ran around the playground

yelling at the top of his voice.

A clause doesn't **have** to make sense as a sentence on its own, but it **can do.**

Q1   Look at these phrases and put a tick by the ones that are **clauses.**

Nigel stirred the soup ✓

with a great big ladle

so it wouldn't be lumpy

bits of carrot and fish heads

floated at the top

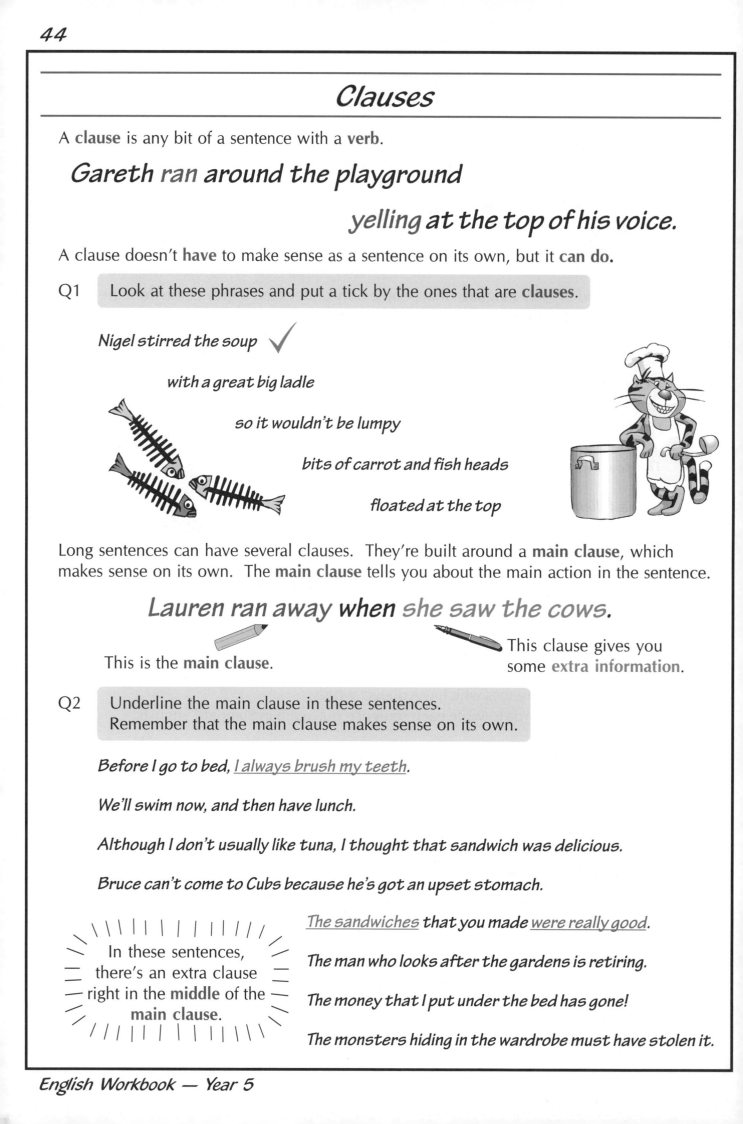

Long sentences can have several clauses. They're built around a **main clause**, which makes sense on its own. The **main clause** tells you about the main action in the sentence.

Lauren ran away **when** she saw the cows.

This is the **main clause**.

This clause gives you some **extra information**.

Q2   Underline the main clause in these sentences.
Remember that the main clause makes sense on its own.

Before I go to bed, <u>I always brush my teeth</u>.

We'll swim now, and then have lunch.

Although I don't usually like tuna, I thought that sandwich was delicious.

Bruce can't come to Cubs because he's got an upset stomach.

In these sentences, there's an extra clause right in the **middle** of the **main clause**.

<u>The sandwiches</u> that you made <u>were really good</u>.

The man who looks after the gardens is retiring.

The money that I put under the bed has gone!

The monsters hiding in the wardrobe must have stolen it.

Joining Clauses

You can join clauses together with **connectives** to make a longer sentence.

Anna and Ben sang *while* they washed the car.

Niall Quinn's disco pants are the best...

Q1 Underline the connectives in these sentences.

You only sing <u>when</u> you're winning.

Andrew walked home because his bike chain had broken.

Ruby couldn't open the door however hard she tried.

Rob and Jen were still laughing and shrieking when they got off the rollercoaster.

Q2 Join three short sentences together with connectives to make one long sentence.

Haresh ate a strawberry ice cream. He bought it from the ice-cream van. He bought it with his pocket money.

<u>Haresh ate a strawberry ice cream which he bought</u>

<u>from the ice-cream van with his pocket money.</u>

Mrs Watson danced to school. She sang "La la la, I'm 40 today." She sang because it was her birthday.

....

....

Becky bought a new game. It was for her computer. She bought it when she was in town.

....

....

I will write to my pen pal. She lives in France. I will write to her after tea.

....

....

More Punctuation

Long sentences with lots of **clauses** often need a bit of punctuation.
Use **commas** to separate the **main clause** from the other clauses.

Damian put on his new shoes, which were very shiny.

Q1 You've looked at commas before, so here are just a few quick questions. Put **commas** in the right places in these sentences.

While you're all here, there's something I want to say to you.

I banged on the door for ages but there was no answer.

I saw Yusuf the other day riding his new bike.

When I find out who broke my stereo they'll be sorry.

Before you sit down make sure your chair isn't broken.

Having read the book I now understand why you said it was exciting.

Use a **colon** when the second bit of the sentence explains the first bit.

At last we found out the truth: there was a thief in the Society.

These two clauses could be **separate sentences**.

Q2 Put **colons** in the right places in these sentences.

Driffield Thursday were facing relegation: they had lost nine of the last ten matches.

The classroom was empty it was a Saturday.

Kim looks just like her mum tall with brown eyes and a jolly smile.

Burt looks just like his dog short fat and with little piggy eyes.

The dog was asleep the long walk had worn him out.

Robbie was starving he'd had nothing to eat since breakfast.

There was a knock at the door a tall green man stood in the doorway.

More Punctuation

A **semicolon** looks like a dot on top of a comma. **Semicolons** are used to join sentences too. They give you a break that's a bit longer than a comma, but shorter than a colon.

The jug toppled over; milk went everywhere.

You can put a semicolon in front of long **fancy conjunctions** like 'otherwise' and 'therefore'.

Keep the motor level; otherwise it won't work.

Q3 Pop a **semicolon** in the right place in these sentences.

Terry stayed up late every night surfing the net; nevertheless, he was always bright and chirpy in the morning.

The winter was cold all the animals were in their burrows, hibernating.

Marcie gave Jo such a lovely present I wish I had thought of something so pretty.

It was an average morning at the office Mark was already complaining.

Dashes are useful when you want to leave a pause between your clauses, like here:

Don't rush — you'll end up making mistakes.

Q4 Join these sentences together with **dashes**.

Mmmmmm... apples...

Hayley's got a new boyfriend. I haven't met him.

Hayley's got a new boyfriend — I haven't met him.

I love fruit. Apples and strawberries are my favourites.

....

He decided to go to Canada instead. I can't remember why.

....

Just write a short letter. It's better than nothing.

....

English Workbook — Year 5

More Prefixes

Prefixes are groups of letters added to the beginnings of words.
Joining 'un-' to the start of a word makes it mean the opposite.

un + intentional ➡ unintentional

Q1 Use the prefix **un-** to make the opposites of these words.

romantic   _unromantic_

impressed   ....

fold   ....

imaginative   ....

important   ....

The prefix '-in' also makes words mean the opposite.

in + sincere ➡ insincere

Q2 Make the opposites of these words by using the prefix **in-**.

hospitable   _inhospitable_

compatible   ....

convenient   ....

visible   ....

capable   ....

Q3 Finish these sentences by making each of the words in brackets into its opposite by using the prefixes **un-** or **in-**.

The students were feeling _unenthusiastic_ (enthusiastic).

This knot looks a bit .... (secure) — I don't trust it.

"That answer is .... (correct)," said the teacher.

This isn't vital — in fact, it's completely .... (important).

"You can all .... (fasten) your seat belts now," said the pilot.

More Prefixes

To make some words easier to say, **in-** sometimes changes to **im-**, **ir-** or **il-**.

Before the letter **r**, **in-** changes to **ir-**.   *regular* ➡ *irregular*

Before the letter **l**, **in-** changes to **il-**.   *legal* ➡ *illegal*

Before the letters **b**, **p** and **m**, **in-** changes to **im-**.
balance ➡ *imbalance*
polite ➡ *impolite*
mortal ➡ *immortal*

Q4 Make the opposites of these words using **in-**, **ir-**, **il-** or **im-**.

active   *inactive*

perfect   ....

legible   ....

curable   ....

mature   ....

logical   ....

responsible   ....

accessible   ....

pure   ....

You can add **pro-** to the start of some nouns to show you think something is a good idea.

Q5 Choose the right word from the box to label the pictures.

pro-bicycle   pro-rhino   ~~pro-peace~~   pro-fishing

pro-peace ➡

⬅ ....

⬅ ....

....

➡ ....

Foreign Words

A lot of words in English have been **borrowed** from other languages.

French   German

En route to get a hamburger,

Kevin saw a crazy kangaroo.

Australian

Q1   Fill in the gap in each sentence with a word from the box that makes sense. All the words have been borrowed from other languages.

> pizza   robot   bungalow   ~~kangaroo~~   kung fu

At the zoo we saw a ___kangaroo___ and loads of koalas.

Sandy knew _____ and so she knew how to fight.

I like all Italian food, but my favourite is _____ .

Inga wants to move into a _____ because she doesn't like stairs.

Bob had always wanted a _____ which would wait on him hand and foot.

Q2   Match the words in the box to the languages they've been borrowed from.

> psychic   villa   abseil   ~~angst~~   champagne   ~~pronto~~   pasta   ~~piano~~
> boutique   restaurant   robot   schnitzel   sombrero   physiotherapy

angst

German

French

Czech

pronto

Spanish

piano

Italian

Greek

Words Ending in '-y'

When you add a suffix to a word ending in -y, the -y sometimes changes to -i.

worry + ed ➥ worried

There's a **consonant** before the -y...

... so **change** the -y to -i.

enjoy + ed ➥ enjoyed

There's a **vowel** before the -y...

...so the -y **doesn't change**.

Q1   Do these word sums to make new words.

happy + ly = ..._happily_.....

Singing happily.

try + ed = ...

deploy + ment = ...

pity + ful = ...

silly + ness = ...

delay + ed = ...

The rule you've just used usually works, **BUT**, if the suffix starts with -i, leave the -y alone.

worry + ing ➥ worrying

Don't change this to -i.

'Worriing' looks silly.

Q2   Fill in the gaps with the -ing form of the verbs in brackets.

I'm ...._studying_.... *(study) tonight, so try not to disturb me.*

Stop .... *(hurry) when you're trying to do something important.*

I'm not .... *(deny) I was there, but I didn't break the vicar's window.*

No one's .... *(bully) me. I just don't like school.*

If a word has only one syllable and ends in -y, then you don't need to change the -y **except** before -**ed** or -**es**.

sly + ly ➥ slyly

Q3   Make new words by solving these word sums.

sky + ward = ..._skyward_....

try + ed = ...

shy + ness = ...

cry + es = ...

shy + ly = ...

dry + ness = ...

Comparatives and Superlatives

When you compare **two** nouns you need a **comparative** adjective.

Swimming is *more enjoyable* than tennis.
Swimming is *better* than tennis.

When you compare **three or more** nouns you need a **superlative** adjective.

Swimming is the *most enjoyable* sport of all.
Swimming is the *best* sport of all.

Q1 Tick the sentences that are right, but put a cross next to the ones that are wrong.

Sam's car is nicer than Jim's. ☑

Tina is the tallest of the two twins. ☐

Joan's car is the most expensive one in town. ☐

My cousin is best at golf than I am. ☐

Only use '**more**' and '**-er**' with '**than**' — never use '**than**' with '**most**' or '**-est**'.

Q2 Underline the correct word(s) to finish each sentence.

This car is (<u>cheaper</u> / cheapest) than those ones standing over there.

I wish I could buy the (most expensive / more expensive) car in the world.

Brenda is the (youngest / younger) in the family.

Brenda is (youngest / younger) than all her brothers and sisters.

You can add **-ish** to the end of a lot of short adjectives. '**Tallish**' means '**quite tall**'.
For some adjectives you have to double the last consonant.

tall + ish ➡ tallish   **big + ish ➡ biggish**

Q3 Make new adjectives from these adjectives by adding **-ish**.

short ....*shortish*....   long ....

thin ....   green ....

Making Nouns

You can make **nouns** from verbs by adding a suffix, but often the spelling changes.

invent ➡ invention   revise ➡ revision

You can add the suffix **-ion** to some verbs to change them into nouns...

...but if the verb ends in **-e**, take the **-e** off first.

Q1 Make nouns from these verbs by adding a suffix.

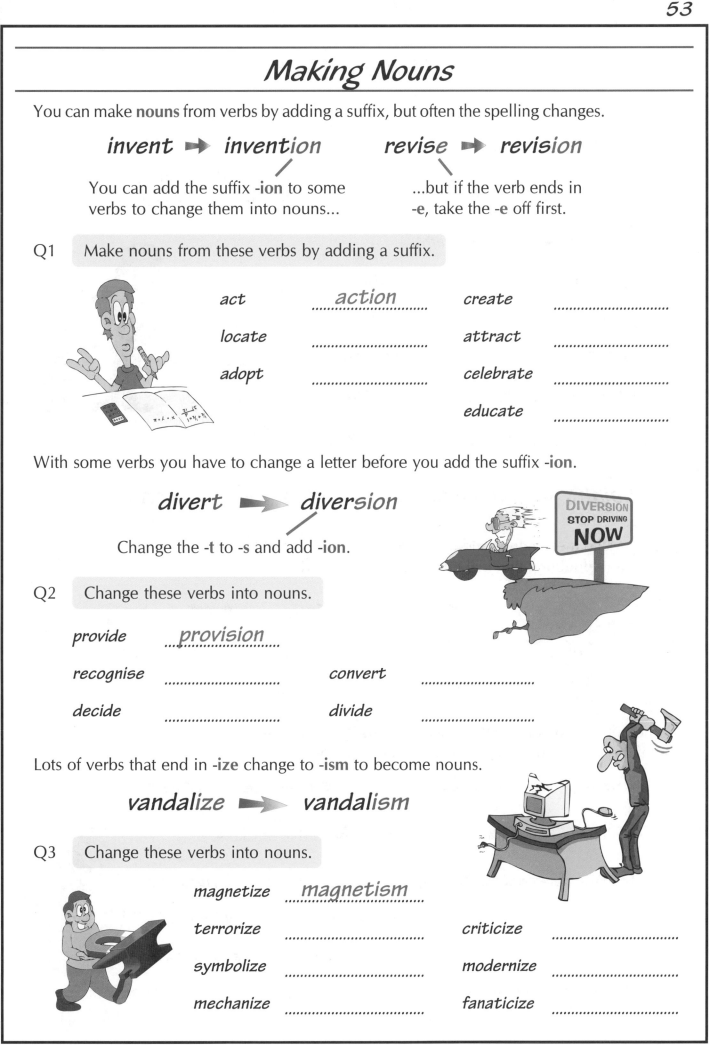

act   *action*   create   ....

locate   ....   attract   ....

adopt   ....   celebrate   ....

                                           educate   ....

With some verbs you have to change a letter before you add the suffix **-ion**.

divert ➡ diversion

Change the **-t** to **-s** and add **-ion**.

Q2 Change these verbs into nouns.

provide   *provision*

recognise ....   convert   ....

decide   ....   divide   ....

Lots of verbs that end in **-ize** change to **-ism** to become nouns.

vandalize ➡ vandalism

Q3 Change these verbs into nouns.

magnetize   *magnetism*

terrorize   ....   criticize ....

symbolize   ....   modernize ....

mechanize   ....   fanaticize ....

Making Verbs

You can make a lot of nouns and adjectives into **verbs** by changing their endings.

serial ➡ **serialize**
For a lot of words, add **-ize** to make a verb.

theory ➡ **theorize**
If the word ends in **-y**, take this off before you add **-ize**.

Q1   Make these nouns into verbs.

sympathy	_sympathize_	critic	....
public	....	motor	....
popular	....	personal	....
category	....	apology	....

Some nouns and adjectives change to verbs if you add **-en**.
For some verbs you have to **double** the **final consonant**.

height ➡ **heighten**   **glad** ➡ **gladden**

Q2   Make these nouns and adjectives into verbs by adding **-en** and doubling the final consonant if you need to.

mad	_madden_	sweet	....
bright	....	short	....
length	....	fat	....

Some nouns and adjectives change to verbs if you add **-ify**.
But if the word ends in **-e**, you have to take that off first.

humid ➡ **humidify**   **false** ➡ **falsify**

Q3   Fill in the gaps with verbs made from the word in brackets.

I can't understand this. Could you ___simplify___ (simple) it for me?

Would you .... (class) this as good, bad or indifferent?

We'll have to .... (pure) this water before we can drink it.

The air in this greenhouse is too dry. You'll have to .... (humid) it.

Standard English

Standard English is 'proper' English — the language people use in schools, business and government. You need to use it for **writing.** All it means is **avoiding** slang and dialect words.

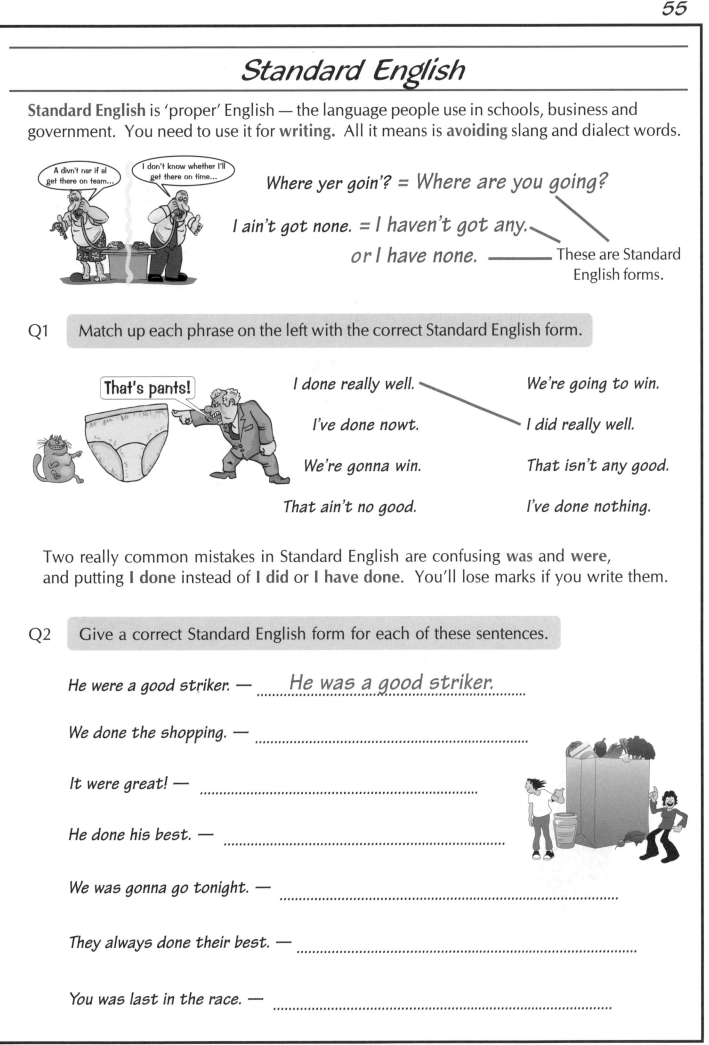

A divn't nar if al get there on team...

I don't know whether I'll get there on time...

Where yer goin'? = Where are you going?

I ain't got none. = I haven't got any.

or I have none. —— These are Standard English forms.

Q1 Match up each phrase on the left with the correct Standard English form.

That's pants!

I done really well. *We're going to win.*

I've done nowt. *I did really well.*

We're gonna win. *That isn't any good.*

That ain't no good. *I've done nothing.*

Two really common mistakes in Standard English are confusing **was** and **were**, and putting **I done** instead of **I did** or **I have done**. You'll lose marks if you write them.

Q2 Give a correct Standard English form for each of these sentences.

He were a good striker. — *He was a good striker.*

We done the shopping. — ....

It were great! — ....

He done his best. — ....

We was gonna go tonight. — ....

They always done their best. — ....

You was last in the race. — ....

Spelling — 'ie' or 'ei'

'i' and 'e' are a real pain for **spelling** when they turn up together in a word.
Just remember this daft little rhyme.

'i' before 'e', except after 'c', but
only when it rhymes with 'bee'.

Now what was it again?...
Me before 'im...
and something...
...about the sea?

Basically, that means it's usually 'ie', but if there's a 'c' before it, it's 'ei'.

Q1 | All of these words have been spelt wrongly.
Write them out again with the correct spellings.

peice: ....*piece*..........

sheild: ....

beleive: ....

releive: ....

cieling: ....

conciet: ....

recieve: ....

acheive: ....

Marble Cake
£1.20 a piece

Watch out for a few sneaky words that **don't** follow the rule.
You've just got to learn them, I'm afraid.

There's nothing weird
about MY ears!

weird   seize   either

Q2 | All of these words have their 'i' and 'e' missing.
Use the spelling rule to fill in the missing letters. Remember the exceptions.

ch..*ie*..f

p..........ce

conc..........t

bel..........ve

n..........ce

w..*ei*..ght

fr..........nd

w..........rd

perc..........ve

shr..........k

br..........f

f..........ld

s..........ge

ach..........ve

A weird chief?

Prepositions

Prepositions are words that tell you the **relationship** of one thing to another.

You went *around* the block.   **I jumped *over* the cat.**

The monkey is *in* the tree.

All these words tell you **where** one thing is **in relation** to something else.

Q1   Underline the preposition in each of these sentences.

Melanie chased me <u>down</u> the hill.

The dog ran under the fence.

Matt climbed up a lamp-post.

Nick sat on the table.

Heathcliff had left the car nearby.

Suzie ran beside Jackie and Corey.

Eugene is under the table.

The gull flew above their heads.

Q2   Fill in each of the gaps with the correct preposition.

I went ...*across*... (across / in) the bridge, then I turned left and went ....

(past / up) the school and .... (down / under) the street towards the church.

Then I climbed .... (into / over) the fence, jumped .... (under / into)

the garden, and scrambled .... (across / up) the tree to our tree-house.

It's easy to get confused between **in** and **into**. Remember, **in** shows position (Sandra was in bed), but **into** is used with moving verbs (I climbed into bed).

Q3   Write either **in** or **into** to complete each sentence.

Henry dived ...*into*... the sea.

He realised there were lots of sharks .... the water.

Henry was .... the sea for five minutes.

The sharks swam towards him so he climbed back .... the boat.

Forming Words

The English language is **changing** all the time. New words are always being formed.
Sometimes the **short version** of a word takes over totally from the original longer word.

fridge
refrigerator

exam
examination

photo
photograph

plane
aeroplane

pub
public house

Q1 Draw lines between the columns to link the short words on the left with their original longer forms on the right.

My 'car has lost its 'motor'!

vet	motorcar
bus	bicycle
phone	veterinary surgeon
car	telephone
bike	omnibus

Some words are made up of the **initials** of the thing they represent.
These words are known as **acronyms**.

PC — Personal Computer

SCUBA — Self-Contained Underwater Breathing Apparatus

Q2 Underline the full, correct meaning of these words.

Tee Hee Hee!

BANG

CD — <u>Compact Disc</u>
    — Crazy Dolphin

LASER — Little Astronauts Sense Earth Refusal
    — Light Amplification by Stimulated Emission of Radiation

Q3 Some new words are created by replacing letters with apostrophes.
Put the apostrophes in the right places to show where letters have been left out.

It was a dark, stormy Hallowe'en night. The church bells chimed midnight, but

Sarah and I weren't afraid. We couldnt let ourselves get frightened because we

were looking for ghosts. "Lets go inside, Im really excited," said Sarah.

"Okay! Well be alright cause Ive got a new torch," I reassured her.

Answers

P1 SYLLABLES
Q1
1: fish, pair, fast
2: woman, apple, prison
3: piano, microscope, aeroplane
Q2
com + pu + ter, fish + ing,
phy + sics, pa + nic, bas + ket,
clev + er + ly
...or any suitable answers.
Q3
but + ter, cun + ning,
pot + ter + y, swim + ming
P2 PLURALS
Q1
dogs, ditches, compasses,
boxes, dresses, bushes,
branches, helmets
Q2
lives, wolves, loaves, wives,
proofs, knives, roofs, chiefs
P3 PLURALS
Q3
✓, ✗ daisies, ✗ flies,
✓, ✗ hobbies, ✓
Q4
The dogs were hiding behind
the trees.
Do you like my favourite toys?
Can you see the fairies in the
gardens?
The dragonflies were hovering
above the ditches.
P4 PREFIXES
Q1
television
telephone
telescope
telesales
telecommunication
selling...
a machine...
communicating...
something...
something...
Q2
bilingual, biplane, bimonthly,
binoculars, bicycle
P5 PREFIXES
Q3
circumference, transatlantic,
translated, transcontinental,
circumnavigation
Q4
automatic, autobiography,
autopilot, autograph,
autofocus
P6 VERBS
Q1
studies, lasts, reads, does,
goes, cooks
Q2
am, are, goes, opens, visits
Q3
is, comes, have, make,
goes, notices
P7 SIMPLIFYING SENTENCES
Q1
say, try, think, make,
watch, happen
Q2
heavy, garden, tired,
happy, hot and dry
P8 PUNCTUATION
Q1
...frightening, John...
...girl, Boris...
...started, eating...
Q2
...exam, Betty...
...homework, Lucy...
...go, there's...

Q3
...Christmas: a bike...
...starving: I...
...following: 6 eggs...
...working: I...
P9 DOUBLE NEGATIVES
Q1
didn't, no; never, no; never,
nobody; doesn't, no
Q2
ever, anything, any, is
Q3
anything, ✓, any, any
P10 VERB TENSES
Q1
present, future, past, present
Q2
We went for a walk.
Sandy slurped soggy semolina.
Ray was on the rampage.
Barry baked buns.
Q3
We are going on holiday.
Dad is driving, Mum is
reading the map and Rita is
singing as loudly as she can. It
is horrible!
P11 AUXILIARY VERBS
Q1
had, was, am, has, is, will
Q2
has, is, was, have
Q3
I am waiting for the bus.
He is cycling all
around the world.
They are writing a play
about a giant hen.
P12 SYNONYMS
Q1
desolate, forlorn, forsaken
uneven, knobbly, rough
amazing, incredible, superb
Q2
Yesterday, Brian Tweeting
proposed to his girlfriend,
Jennifer Lee. Brian, 21, is the
main singer of the well-known
band, the Condiment Boyz,
while Jennifer is an actress.
The delighted couple said they
were really thrilled, as they
flew to Las Vegas to get
married at once.
... or any suitable answer.
P13 ROOT WORDS
Q1
help, know, faith, person,
emotion, friend
Q2
easy
sleep
enthusiastic
force
prison
jail
keen
simple
rest
power

Q3
nonsense, sensible
forecast, castaway
superhero, heroic
outcast, outside
forceful, reinforce
...or any suitable answers.

P14 SPEECH
Q1
"I'm a Martian!"
"No, you're not!"
"I'm dressed up as one though."
"Yes, but it's a terrible costume"
Q2
...tank," said...
...asked, "Has...
...screamed, "Don't...
...longer," Esther...
...day," said...
...wistfully, "Me...
P15 SPEECH
Q3
"I don't think we should pick
Harry for the team," said Marvin.
"Why not?" asked Jerry.
"He's always late for
practice," replied Marvin.
"That's true," agreed Jerry.
Q4
Milly said that she was going
to win the jelly-eating contest.
Ann said that she could eat a
lot more jelly than Milly.
Mum said that everybody
should eat vegetables instead
of jelly.
P16 IDIOMS
Q1
get yourself into some very
hot water, flogging a dead
horse, beating about the bush,
taking you for a ride, get your
skates on
Q2
toe the line
par for...
wind...
pay through...
throw in...
make a clean...
that's...
annoy...
follow...
give up
to confess...
pay...
Q3
horns, hatchet,
wet blanket, dead horse
P17 IDIOMS
Q4
2, 1, 3, 5, 4
Q5
paid through the nose for it,
bury the hatchet, out of the
frying pan and into the fire,
under a cloud
P18 1ST, 2ND, & 3RD PERSON
Q1
I was playing the trombone.
We are fighting.
I will eat all the pies.
I like arm-wrestling.
Q2
You want to build a castle.
You need a new hat.
You always eat cheese.
You play rugby.
Q3
They play golf.
She prefers chess.
He hates all sport.
They like netball.
P19 1ST, 2ND & 3RD PERSON
Q4
buy, eats, am eating, goes,
Are you going, is buying

Q5
We are going water-skiing in
Hawaii next week.
Darren goes tap-dancing in
London every evening.
I am waiting for the last bus home.
You are wearing your new
jacket today.
P20 RHYMES
Q1
crocodile, Nile; tail, scale;
grin, in; claws, jaws
Q2
✗, ✓, ✓, ✗, ✓, ✗
Q3
rhyme, half rhyme, rhyme
rhyme, half rhyme, rhyme
P21 RHYMES
Q4
in, thin; out, stout;
I, by; me, story; I, die
Q5
towers, twisted, breeze, grows
scared, trace, loss
sand, salt, funny, many
...or any suitable answers.
P22 ADVERBS ABOUT TALKING
Q1
noisily, hopelessly, cheerfully,
sadly, furiously, timidly
Q2
announced calmly,
asked pleasantly, yelled
ecstatically, snapped angrily,
piped innocently
...or any suitable answers.
P23 WORD ORDER
Q1
The dog barked at the cat.
My aunt gave me a bar of
chocolate.
Tigers and gibbons live in the
forests of Borneo.
Q2
A huge chicken put my uncle
on the barbecue. Mars
landed on the spaceship.
The flounder caught a
gigantic fisherman.
...or any suitable answers.
P24 WRITING INSTRUCTIONS
Q1
Find, polish, cover, stand
back, Ask, Be careful
Q2
Any suitable answers are
acceptable.
P25 SAYING WHAT'S HAPPENED
Q1
conquered, were, built, joined,
made, attacked, ordered
Q2
went, could, called, was,
used, had, wore, made,
fastened
P26 SPELLING RULES
Q1
careful, playful, cheerful,
tearful, thankful, harmful,
hopeful, useful, spoonful,
powerful

Q2
hard, soft, hard, soft, soft,
hard, soft, soft, hard, soft,
hard, hard
P27 SUFFIXES
Q1
attention
tension
television
fraction
optician
extension
Indonesian
action
-cian
-sian
-sion
-tion
Q2
education, Asian,
concentration, illustration,
magician, decision, politician,
television, temptation
P28 DOUBLE LETTERS
Q1
hotter, swimming, padded,
wetter, betting, batted,
flatter, fatten
Q2
waded, wagged, wagging,
bitter, siting
P29 DOUBLE LETTERS
Q3
ticked, pained, feeling,
wrecked
matted, caller
digger, builder, smelling,
talked
Q4
taller, grilled, exclaimed,
ruler, picked, hurled,
dipped, lined
P30 FOUR KINDS OF NOUN
Q1
frog, basket, boat, rice, lily
Q2
Proper nouns: Thames,
Alaska, Jeremy, Titanic
Common nouns: hairdrier,
target, tractor, chair
P31 FOUR KINDS OF NOUN
Q3
a herd of
a flock of
a gang of
a fleet of
a pack of
a shoal of
a troop of
thieves
sheep
monkeys
wolves
elephants
fish
ships
Q4
dread, fear, cowardice,
fun, peace, quiet
P32 FIRST, SECOND & THIRD PERSON
Q1
near, good, off, hair, dude,
tough, mud, blow, new
Q2
pear, wool, sew, watch,
though, prove
Q3
read, bread; foot, boot; new,
sew; fork, work
P33 ANTONYMS
Q1
near
good
big
dangerous
hot
safe
far
cold
small
bad

Answers are always given column by column, not row by row.

Answers

Q2
fish, banana, book, egg, wall, green

Q3
right: left, wrong
light: dark, heavy
happy: unhappy, sad
stop: start, go
miss: catch, hit

P34 UNCLEAR SENTENCES
Q1
I would like a hot cross bun.
Cake is my favourite food.
Dave was watching TV so his dad told him off.
...or any suitable answers.

Q2
The police shot a man who was carrying a knife.
FOR SALE: Goat: good with children, eats anything
KEEP MEDICINES SAFE. Lock medicines away if you have children in the house.
...or any suitable answers.

P35 ONOMATOPOEIA
Q1
C, B, A, D

Q2
croak, popped, fizzed, creaked, coughing

Q3
ploosh, tharupped, thunk, scrawl
... or any suitable answers.

P36 HOMOPHONES
Q1
bread, grate, reins

Q2
maid, made; dear, deer;
bored, board; knot, not

Q3
find, which, would, to, son, seen, know

P37 METAPHORS
Q1
S, M, S, M

Q2
The moon was a giant white dinner plate in the sky.
She is a spoilt princess.
The tree was a scarecrow in the moonlight.

Q3
turkey, sunshine, angel

P38 PRONOUNS
Q1
it, they, him, mine

Q2
she, yours, it, they

Q3
Ferdie, Wanda, Jonah, this music

P39 WORDS ENDING IN '-E'
Q1
useless, skating, hopeful, sloping, making, hopeless, driving, lifeless

Q2
smiling, rising, joking, coming

Q3
completely, baking, tasteless, decorating

P40 APOSTROPHES
Q1
Kelly's, Tom's, Mark's, Sarah's, Rob's, Will's

Q2
Marcus's, Lewis's, James's, Chris's

Q3
wolves', rats', lions', dogs'

P41 APOSTROPHES
Q4
Don't tell Katy what I've got for her birthday. It's meant to be a surprise.
I can't tell what I'm supposed to do.
We're going to be late if you don't hurry up.
The film wasn't very good.
If you've watched the film, you'll know why I didn't like it.

Q5
It's, its, it's, it's, its

P42 UNSTRESSED VOWELS
Q1
elephant, interesting, metal, strengthen, even, cauldron

Q2
interest, catalogue, common, patient, totally, categories, variety, personal, fortunately, spaniel, constantly, caterpillar

Q3
poisonous, Elephants, enormous, Novelists, describe, varieties

P43 DIALECT WORDS
Q1
mash — going
grockles — stream
beck — brew
gannin — you'll
Tha'll — tourists

Q2
We're off to the church now.
Did you see that fellow with the green hat?
Where's the child gone?
Mick's hiding in the alley.

P44 CLAUSES
Q1
Nigel stirred the soup
so it wouldn't be lumpy
floated at the top

Q2
I always brush my teeth.
We'll swim now.
I thought that sandwich was delicious.
Bruce can't come to Cubs.
The sandwiches were really good.
The man is retiring.
The money has gone!
The monsters must have stolen it.

P45 JOINING CLAUSES
Q1
when, because, however, when

Q2
Haresh ate a strawberry ice cream which he bought from the ice cream van with his pocket money.
Mrs Watson sang "La la la, I'm 40 today," as she danced to school, because it was her birthday.
cont.

Becky bought a new game for her computer when she was in town.
I will write to my pen pal, who lives in France, after tea.
...or any suitable answers.

P46 MORE PUNCTUATION
Q1
...here, there's...
...ages, but...
...day, riding...
...stereo, they'll...
...down, make...
...book, I...

Q2
...relegation: they...
...empty: it...
...mum: tall...
...dog: short...
...asleep: the...
...starving: he'd...
...door: a...

P47 MORE PUNCTUATION
Q3
...net; nevertheless...
...cold; all...
...present; I...
...office; Mark...

Q4
...boyfriend — I...
...fruit — apples...
...instead — I...
...letter — it's...

P48 MORE PREFIXES
Q1
unromantic, unimpressed, unfold, unimaginative, unimportant

Q2
inhospitable, incompatible, inconvenient, invisible, incapable

Q3
unenthusiastic, insecure, incorrect, unimportant, unfasten

P49 MORE PREFIXES
Q4
inactive, imperfect, illegible, incurable, immature, illogical, irresponsible, inaccessible, impure

Q5
pro-peace, pro-bicycle, pro-rhino, pro-fishing

P50 FOREIGN WORDS
Q1
kangaroo, kung fu, pizza, bungalow, robot

Q2
German: angst, abseil, schnitzel
Czech: robot
Greek: psychic, physiotherapy
Italian: piano, villa, pasta
Spanish: pronto, sombrero
French: champagne, boutique, restaurant

P51 WORDS ENDING IN '-Y'
Q1
happily, tried, deployment, pitiful, silliness, delayed

Q2
studying, hurrying, denying, bullying

Q3
skyward, tried, shyness, cries, shyly, dryness

P52 COMPARATIVES AND SUPERLATIVES
Q1
✓, ✗, ✓, ✗

Q2
cheaper, most expensive, youngest, younger

Q3
shortish, thinnish, longish, greenish

P53 MAKING NOUNS
Q1
action, location, adoption, creation, attraction, celebration, education

Q2
provision, recognition, decision, conversion, division

Q3
magnetism, terrorism, symbolism, mechanism, criticism, modernism, fanaticism

P54 MAKING VERBS
Q1
sympathize, publicize, popularize, categorize, criticize, motorize, personalize, apologize
-ise endings are also acceptable.

Q2
madden, brighten, lengthen, sweeten, shorten, fatten

Q3
simplify, classify, purify, humidify.

P55 STANDARD ENGLISH
Q1
I done really well. — We're...
I've done nowt. — I...
We're gonna win. — That...
That ain't no good. — I've...

Q2
He was a good striker.
We did the shopping.
It was great!
He did his best.
We were going to go tonight.
They always did their best.
You were last in the race.

P56 SPELLING — 'IE' OR 'EI'
Q1
piece, shield, believe, relieve, ceiling, conceit, receive, achieve

Q2
chief, piece, conceit, believe, niece, weight, weird, shriek, field, achieve, friend, perceive, brief, siege

P57 PREPOSITIONS
Q1
down, under, up, on, nearby, beside, under, above

Q2
across, past, down, over, into, up

Q3
into, in, in, into

P58 FORMING WORDS
Q1
vet — veterinary surgeon
bus — omnibus
phone — telephone
car — motorcar
bike — bicycle

Q2
Compact Disc,
Light Amplification by Stimulated Emission of Radiation

Q3
Hallowe'en, weren't, couldn't, Let's, I'm, We'll, 'cause, I've

Answers are always given column by column, not row by row.